Develop
YOUR
Teaching

A professional development
pack for mathematics – and other – teachers

THE MATHEMATICAL ASSOCIATION
AND STANLEY THORNES (PUBLISHERS) LTD

First published in 1991 by:
Stanley Thornes (Publishers) Ltd
Old Station Drive
Leckhampton
CHELTENHAM GL53 0DN
England

British Library Cataloguing in Publication Data
Develop your teaching: A professional development
pack for mathematics (and other) teachers.
  I. The Mathematical Association
  371.1

ISBN 07487 0530 9

Designed and typeset by Oxprint Ltd, Oxford

Printed and bound in Great Britain by Martins of Berwick

Have you ever sat with a group of friends who are relating experiences, and suddenly felt the need to tell your own story?

What is it that makes us so eager to share our own stories in this way? Perhaps something has been said which strikes a deeper chord of understanding in ourselves, allowing us to resonate with the total group feeling. In order to share our feelings with the group we tell an anecdote from our own past. The telling of the story has its own therapeutic value, and most of these swapped tales are soon forgotten.

However, bringing discipline to the story-telling activity can lead to identifying what that group feeling is, and that can lead to issues to work on.

As a working group of mathematics educators, we tried to identify the conditions under which these anecdotes flow freely – for example the 'warmth' of group feeling seemed to be an important characteristic. We also developed strategies for identifying underlying concerns.

When teacher groups meet together there are common areas of concern that exist within the group. This pack is intended to help find ways to uncover, bring to the surface, those that the group feel are important.

Preface

The authors of this pack first came together as a working group of the Mathematical Association in 1985 to think about Cockcroft 243 and its manifestation in the classroom. At that time we were particularly interested in the close interactions between teachers and pupils and in how the Cockcroft elements of *exposition*, *discussion*, *practical work*, *consolidation* and *practice*, *problem solving*, and *investigation* entered into such interactions. We believed, and still do, that every teacher needs to develop their own concepts of what the Cockcroft elements mean and to work on their own interpretations for the classroom.

However, we quickly realised that abstract talk about *investigation*, or about *discussion* was unhelpful as each of us might have a very different understanding of these terms. What was especially helpful was when someone told a story of some incident which had happened to them in a professional capacity, as this created a particular focus to which others could relate. Such stories, or *anecdotes*, rapidly became central to our discussion and thinking. As one person told an anecdote others found themselves responding with related anecdotes and this had two important effects.

1. It brought us closer as a group. It raised the level of *warmth* in the group. It helped us to come to a clearer understanding of what concerned us.

2. From a succession of anecdotes it was possible to trace an underlying pattern of sameness from which we were able to identify issues which were of common concern. Having a sense of the underlying issues was a first step in getting at some of our own fundamental concerns and bringing these into the open.

Subtly our focus began to change and we found ourselves moving away from thinking directly about Cockcroft 243 towards consideration of *a way of working* through which issues (such as those related to Cockcroft 243) could be raised. We identified a strengthening belief that our way of working together was of immense value, enabling us to bring to consciousness our own concerns and thereby helping us to develop professionally.

We wanted to explore whether it would be possible to offer our perceived way of working to others who had not been part of our developing thinking. So, with the help of Mathematics Adviser Geoff Faux, we organised a conference with a group of teachers in Cumbria. Despite reservations to do with the artificial nature of coming together for just a weekend, we found the experience both rewarding and encouraging. We were able to refine our perceptions of the way of working, and a year later we held a second conference, this time with the help of another Mathematics Adviser, Peter Reynolds, in Suffolk. Our feelings were greatly enhanced and reinforced and we went from the Suffolk conference into writing this pack.

We were fortunate in gaining the financial support of the Training Agency's TVEI Unit. Their declared objective of 'enabling young people to learn *how* to be effective, solve problems, work in teams, be enterprising and creative through the *way* they are taught' is much in sympathy with the way of working we are proposing in this pack.

What you find here is the result of collaborative work by a team of nine people. There is much scope for experimentation and further research. It will be your own interpretation of the process that will have the greatest relevance to your own situation.

Barbara Jaworski (*Chair of the T.I.M.E. subcommittee*)

The production team

This pack has been produced by the T.I.M.E.[1] subcommittee of Teaching Committee of the Mathematical Association, which included the following members:

Janet Duffin	Wendy Garrard
Nick James	Barbara Jaworski (Chair)
Harriet Marland	Anne Tyson
David Wooldridge	Rod Young.

The writing of the pack was done by Janet Duffin, Nick James, Barbara Jaworski, Harriet Marland, David Wooldridge, Rod Young, Sue Young.

The production of the pack was financed jointly by the Mathematical Association and the TVEI Unit of the Training Agency. It was managed by Sue Young who also edited written materials.

We are grateful to many teachers from Cumbria, Suffolk, Bedfordshire, Cambridgeshire and Hertfordshire for their participation in research and their helpful suggestions. In particular we should like to thank, Julie Winyard, Brian Bell, Jacqui Fuller, Neil Kitching, Terry Andrews and Ann Freeman who read and commented on drafts of the pack; and Pat Woods, Anne Barber, Lyn Hodgkinson, Janet Ridge and pupils of Harlington Upper School, Bedfordshire, for contributing anecdotes.

We are indebted to Geoff Faux and Peter Reynolds for their help and comments throughout the project and their critical reading of various drafts of writing.

We should also like to thank Dave Carter who acted as critical reader for the Mathematical Association and provided valuable help and advice.

Please address all correspondence to the Mathematical Association, 259 London Road, Leicester LE2 3BE (0533 703877).

---

1 T.I.M.E. stands for Teacher-centred Inservice in Mathematics Education.

Use of this pack

This pack is about a way of working in which teachers can engage in order to further their own professional development. Each part is a collection of writings by different members of the M.A. writing team. Differences in style and overlap of content are deliberate. We believe that these add to the richness of presentation and reinforce the importance of individual response to the processes described. Moreover, this allows each part to stand as a discreet entity, for although the pack has its own linearity forced by one piece of writing having to be either before or after another, there is no intention that you will start at the beginning and read straight through to the end. You will find that some of the parts are about working practically, while others are concerned with the theory behind the processes. We recommend that you dip into it at a place which interests you and from there follow references to other sections.

The pack proposes a *way of working* in which anecdotes or experiences, presented in a variety of ways, are exchanged and from which issues of concern may be identified for action. An essential aspect is the formation of a group of teachers who will work together. Even *two* teachers would be enough to make a start. An obvious reason for this is that it is very hard to exchange anecdotes with yourself, or to work alone on your own anecdotes. The pack contains many examples of how groups of teachers have worked together, and Part III particularly concentrates on the nature of group working and the role of group leader. Section 5, 'Weekend diary of a group leader', might be one place to start.

If you would like to read an account of the way of working proposed, you could turn directly to Part IV. However, we suggest that, in the first instance, this rather abstract account may not be very meaningful, and that reading some of the case studies in Part II to get a sense of the way of working in action might be more valuable.

Parts V and VII consider the use of the way of working as it might be applied to practical situations which teachers would find valuable. In Part V, the focus is a variety of *areas of concern*, i.e. the *application* of the way of working to, for example, *concerns* about assessment, or about the National Curriculum, or about cross-curricular initiatives. Part VII focuses on a variety of inservice *events* and shows how this way of working might be used in different kinds of sessions whose aim is professional development.

Although the work has its origin in Mathematics Education, the way of working proposed is neither linked nor limited to Mathematics *per se*. It has potential to transcend subject boundaries and has a powerful use where teachers in different subject areas or phases of education wish to work together to reach for common issues. The TVEI unit of the Training Agency have recognised this in a fundamental way by providing funding for the production of the pack, and we are grateful for their support and confidence. This has led to us look at issues more widely than just the teaching of mathematics, and evidence of this will be found in some of the more general examples and anecdotes in Parts VII and VIII.

The pack is deliberately presented in loose leaf format so that you can add your own perceptions, reflections, plans, anecdotes and so on. It may be possible to publish a postscript for later addition to the pack consisting of contributions from its users. If you have such a contribution please let us have it via the Mathematical Association (address on page 1).

Contents

I WANT TO TELL YOU A STORY . . .

Part I introduces the notion of anecdotes, on which the proposed way of working is based.

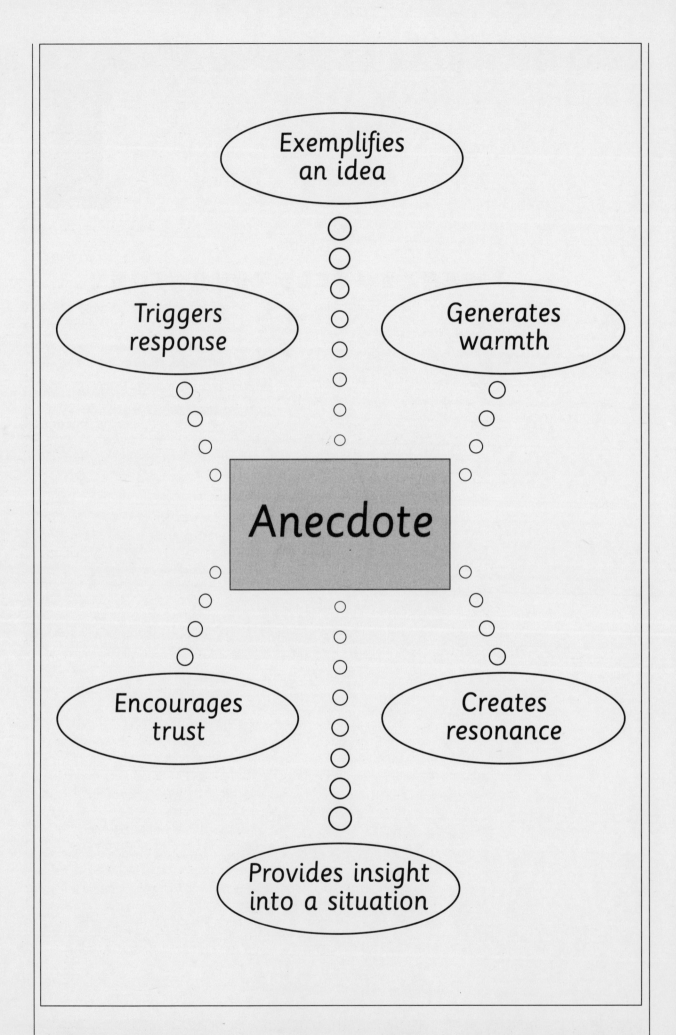

It is lunchtime. A few teachers have gathered in the staffroom. Some have started to eat sandwiches. Another teacher comes in, flops into a chair alongside several colleagues, and says, 'Do you know what just happened in my lesson . . . ?'

Do you recognise the scenario described above? In particular, have you been part of staffroom conversations where teachers have told stories about events from their lessons? Have you indeed told such stories yourself? If possible, think back to the last time this happened. Can you recall the story you told?

Such a story might be referred to as an *anecdote*. This pack is concerned with a way of working which capitalises on the custom of teachers to share such stories or anecdotes.

WHAT DO WE MEAN BY AN ANECDOTE?

The staffroom scenario at the start of this section is itself an anecdote. In writing it we hoped that the words 'It is lunchtime . . .' would evoke in you a sense of your own staffroom from which you could picture what followed – the teacher coming in, sitting down, starting to relate an incident from her lesson. Of course, her *story* about the incident is also an anecdote – the *teacher's* anecdote.

Have you ever experienced, when someone spontaneously offers some story of their own experience, that you feel a strong sense of having been there too? You recognise what the person is saying because in some way it speaks to your own experience. You might respond with something like, 'Oh yes! I know exactly what you are talking about!' You might then go on to offer a story of your own in response.

In this pack we are interested in anecdotes not for their own sake so much as in their power to generate this sort of response in another person.

Effectively, the response comes from relating what is heard to one's own experience. The response is triggered by a *resonance* in the person responding – rather like musical resonance, *striking a chord*.

ANECDOTES SPAWN ANECDOTES

As one teacher tells a tale, another responds and another and so on. If you have been in such a situation, you may be familiar with the warmth which is generated among a group as incidents are recalled and shared. The feeling of warmth is very important, drawing colleagues together and enhancing the sharing and support that is so necessary for professional development.

It is the purpose of this pack to suggest that the inherent property of anecdotes, to generate such a warmth of response, can be harnessed to promote a more *conscious* understanding of teaching and learning. Much of teaching is at an intuitive level. Experienced teachers develop successful ways of working in the classroom with pupils; but it is often hard to identify just what it is that creates this success. When things go wrong, it can be even harder to pinpoint what might have been better.

BEWARE ANECDOTE LUST

The raising of the intuitive to the conscious does not usually happen just as a result of a succession of anecdotes. In fact dwelling in and with the anecdotes can be an indulgence (hence the subheading *anecdote lust!*). What we should like to suggest is that there is a disciplined way of working on anecdotes which can lead to a more conscious understanding of what teaching actually means. Briefly, this involves identifying issues which underlie the anecdotes being shared; refining these issues and considering what consequences there might be for your classroom; and finally instigating some classroom action which might ultimately improve your teaching.

HOW THIS PACK CAN HELP

The pack explores this way of working as follows.

- *It gives particular examples of anecdotes and the issues which can be raised, by describing actual occasions when teachers have worked in this way. These will be found chiefly in Part II, with further examples in Parts V and VII.*

- *By detailing, formally, a process – the* anecdoting *process – for generating and working on anecdotes to raise issues about teaching and to enable you to develop your own work in the classroom. This is done in Part IV.*

- *By suggesting ways in which you and your colleagues might begin to work on anecdotes yourselves. This is covered in Parts III, V and VII.*

- *By providing a unifying theory which links the anecdoting process to investigative approaches in the classroom and to a consistent approach to learning at many levels. This is done in Part VI.*

- *By providing anecdotes and resources which you can use to get started on working in this way with your own colleagues. You will find these in Part VIII.*

II

A WAY OF WORKING – ANECDOTES IN ACTION

Part II describes a number of sessions in which teachers shared anecdotes of their classroom experience and sought out issues which were of concern to them as a step towards developing their own classroom practice.

The purpose is to introduce the anecdoting process through examples of its use, before looking at the process itself later in Part IV.

Contents

Introduction

Teachers often come up with anecdotes, or tales from their day to day classroom experiences. Telling them to their colleagues is important. It is a way of getting things off one's chest. But it can become much more than that.

Pause for a moment and reflect on recent conversations with friends. Much conversation is concerned with anecdotes. One person recounts a recent event. This sparks off a similar story in the listener and so there is an exchange of anecdotes. More often than not there is an underlying sameness linking all these brief but vivid accounts. When the people involved part, declaring how they all seem to be 'on the same wavelength', they are, in fact, implicitly alluding to this sameness. However, in everyday life it is usually neither necessary nor relevant to take the matter any further by attempting to raise this subconscious sense of agreement with one's friends up to a level of consciousness. One just does not normally identify and make explicit what the sameness is underpinning all that was said.

Such sameness is often intuitively identified when someone in conversation talks of 'changing the subject'. This implies that they identify some common theme which has been running through the conversation up to that point, and that what they have to say is no longer a part of this theme.

What Part II attempts to show is how one can capitalise on the fact that teachers *do* swap anecdotes with their colleagues. They do so all the time. If, however, someone intervenes at an appropriate stage to invite the group to identify the 'topic of conversation' running through a recently aired collection of anecdotes, it is possible to make that topic explicit. Once done, the whole group will have identified a common issue of note or concern and they can then pause to consider what action they might take as a consequence.

Here, then, is a potential way of enabling teachers to pinpoint areas of concern and to work positively on them. We should like to suggest that the process, moving from anecdotes to classroom action, is at the heart of sound school-based professional development. What is more, once colleagues have acquired some experience of the process illustrated in this chapter and seen its potential for improving their classroom practice, it can become a regular way of working – a form of on-going professional development for the group concerned.

Part II is split up into four sections, each giving particular examples of teachers working with anecdotes. Taken together they show how a process of on-going professional development might be introduced into one's own situation.

- *The first section is an activity, using a video excerpt, which illustrates the notion that there are 'topics of conversation' underpinning people's anecdotes. In response to a piece of video tape which they had just watched, two teachers, Manjit and George, shared anecdotes with their group. You are invited to identify some issue implicit in what Manjit and George shared.*

- *The second section describes how one group of teachers moved through the whole process – using written anecdotes, from other teachers, to spawn related anecdotes of their own, and so to the identification of underlying issues to work on in their classrooms.*

- *The third section gives a higher order perspective. Not only does it illustrate the move from anecdote to issue, it also shows how a group really needs to commit itself to at least three sessions before the value of the approach becomes fully apparent.*

- *The fourth and final section describes the other side of the coin – when sessions do not take off as expected but turn out to be surprisingly fruitful.*

How might I instigate such on-going professional development in my own school situation?

From video-image to issue – an activity for *you* to do now

▨ *To get a feel for the way in which a teacher's anecdote can lead to other teachers sharing accounts of events of their own situations, highlighting an area of concern for all of them, read what happened in the following event. A group of teachers had watched a short video excerpt showing part of a lesson where five children, aged 9 or 10, were estimating the weights of a collection of parcels and then weighing them to check out their guesstimates.*

In the discussion which followed the viewing, two teachers Manjit and George, offered anecdotes from their own experience. See if you[1] can detect any underlying sameness in the stories shared by Manjit and George.

At first, the discussion which followed the viewing of the video centred on what the teachers had *actually* seen. Having first of all noted down what each individually recalled seeing, they then moved to a collective view of the video excerpt. They identified details of what the children had been doing, the way they'd been working, and the direction and intervention of the class teacher.

This clearly struck a chord with one of the group, Manjit. She began to say how the idea of 'teacher direction' made her *think*.

'Time is so important . . . children need time . . . without teacher interfering.'

Still referring to the video, Tim, the group leader, asked her how *she* would achieve this. Manjit replied. 'Well . . . just giving them more time. Time's so important . . . they need time to talk out their own thoughts. I feel as a teacher I interfere too much. I would have just put out the equipment and let them explore it.'

Tim responded by asking Manjit if she could give an example by describing something she had done recently. 'Yes, a *for instance*' said George.

Manjit's anecdote

Well, I had set six children from my class the task of making biscuits for the whole class of thirty. I told them to make one biscuit each for the rest of the class and two each for the bakers, making thirty-six biscuits in total. I was busy so I let them get on with it. When they had finished they told me they had made one hundred and six biscuits. I wasn't really cross but these are five year olds and I had planned to arrange the results in three sets of ten with six over and then to talk about number and tens and units.

---

1 You might be the reader. Taking part in this activity as you read could help you as an individual to get a sense of what we mean by the underlying 'sameness' in anecdotes. Alternatively you could offer the activity to a group of colleagues for their consideration and discussion.

John said 'But we didn't want to make thirty-six.'
I explained to him that it would take a very long time
to draw the necessary sets of ten on the board. 'But you
won't have to,' he replied. 'Just write 10 the right
number of times and then add up in 10s.' He had clearly
thought out something I had not put into his mind, in
order to help me. We had, admittedly, already talked
about the symbol 0 and how much easier it is to write 10
than ten tallies, but I had forgotten this. My chance
busyness had given the children time to themselves and
allowed this happy accident to happen when in the normal
way I would have interrupted. John's response made me
very happy.

After a moment's reflection, George said 'Can you always afford time? In secondary schools we tend to be governed by a syllabus we have to get through. I am always conscious of rushing things through, of having to direct more.'

'Do you have a contrary instance in that case; an example of something that went wrong?' asked Tim.

George's anecdote

Yes, I had been trying to find time to work on something that was not
part of the stipulated curriculum. We had been working for six weeks
on the Nemesis Trail, a competition from the calculator people,
Casio. This had proved most enjoyable and at the end I decided to let
the children make their own mathematical trails in the play area to
challenge each other. Unfortunately, the day I'd set aside to do the
trails was wet and miserable, but I felt that already too much time
had been given to this activity and so I went ahead — and a lot of
very good work was ruined! I had wanted to get it done on that day
so that I could move on to the next topic . . . I constantly have
that feeling with a lot of project-type work that I have got to speed
up on it so I can go back to the syllabus.

> *Spend a few moments trying to identify any underlying sameness in these two anecdotes. Then try and write down what you think the 'topic of conversation' was all about. Does this look like an issue or area of concern for the teachers involved? Suggest further activities in the classroom exploring what could be done about the issue identified.*

COMMENT ON THE ACTIVITY

It is not appropriate for us now to find a definitive answer to what you were asked to do. That would be playing the game of guess what was in the author's mind! What *is* important though is that you recognise the importance of the 'abstractor role' you have just played. In effect you listened to what Manjit and George said and tried to abstract any underlying sameness in their stories. Bringing this out into the open identified a potential issue of concern to both of them. They could then be challenged to say what they would go away and *do* about it in their classrooms. They might also be encouraged to come back in a few weeks to share how they had been getting on.

Without such effort on your part (or Tim's) to identify the underlying issues, the discussion between Manjit and George and the group is left in the realm of a 'good chat'. However, by doing what you did in this activity, the matter can be taken a whole lot further perhaps enabling the teachers concerned to formulate new views on the pace of both individual lessons and syllabus content to be covered. That would be significant professional development indeed – and especially relevant to TVEI objectives for cross-curricular work and to coverage of the National Curriculum Targets!

From written anecdotes to issues

This is an account of the movement and pace through a one and a half hour conference session involving both primary and secondary teachers. Jane, the group leader, intervenes to encourage identification of issues as you were encouraged to do in Section 1 above.

THE START OF THE SESSION

A group of six teachers sat down together. One of them, Jane, the group leader, had a number of sheets of paper on each of which were written three anecdotes. She gave one sheet to each person and suggested that they should:

- *individually read the three anecdotes;*

- *each focus on one anecdote and on aspects of their own experience which the anecdote brought to mind;*

- *after a minute or two of silent individual reflection, share their thoughts with a neighbour.*

In silence, they began to read the anecdotes[1] which are printed below:

1. Danny

I observed a teacher, Helena, with a group of reception class pupils making bead chains. The beads were of many colours, some spherical, some cubical. A boy, Danny, came shyly up to her and showed her his chain.

She praised him, saying how good it looked, and started to ask him some questions about it. Most of the questions were to do with 'how many?' — how many yellow beads, how many cubical beads, how many different colours? He answered the questions, apparently without any difficulty.

Then she said, 'How many more yellow ones are there than red ones?'

Danny looked puzzled, so she repeated the question. His answer was seven, which was the number of red beads.

I was waiting for her next question. How would she help him to see the difference? She ruffled his hair, said that he had done well and asked if he would like to take part in another activity.

---

1 These are taken from Jaworski, 1989 (see Part VIII.)

2. Investigations

```
The way I work with these things [investigations] is that if I know
too much about where it's going, I may well prod and guide people
into directions which may not be the most fruitful or the most
interesting ones for them.

Vicky and Anne were actually working in a way which I thought was not
very fruitful.

I haven't prodded them very much. I haven't guided them very much.

And the fact that Anne had said a few things earlier on in the
[whole-class part of the] lesson helped actually, because I was able
to say, 'What was your idea?'

I don't know. There are times when you should [prod and guide] . . .
after all I'm supposed to be the 'teacher', and sometimes I know that
some ways are more fruitful than others . . . . It's terribly
difficult.
```

3. Panic

```
I've never taught this topic before, and I'm not very confident about
it. I prepared myself thoroughly by reading a number of books, but I
couldn't bring myself to make it as open-ended as I usually do. I
taught it very straight from the blackboard and didn't really invite
questions. When Elizabeth asked a question that I didn't know the
answer to I nearly panicked. But I was able to invite the rest of the
class to comment on the question, and Nelista said something that I
realised was right and so I took it from there and it was OK.
```

Although Jane had gathered and supplied the three anecdotes it was still possible to take part fully herself. She chose the second anecdote on which to work, and recalled a particular event which took place in her secondary classroom the previous week. She could remember it vividly because it had raised some important questions for her at the time. As she recalled it, she was able to remember some of her own words, and words of the pupils she had been working with. Replaying it in her mind brought the event back sharply into focus.

FROM INDIVIDUAL THINKING TO DISCUSSION IN PAIRS

Jane, as group leader, kept her eye on the others in the group, and when she noticed eyes start to be raised and to look around, she made a motion towards her own neighbour. The others followed suit, the group moved naturally into pairs and conversation began. Her partner, Mary, had in fact also chosen anecdote (2) on which to focus. She said that the words *investigation* and *prod* and *guide* had triggered off an association for her. 'It reminded me of an investigation that I did with my class last week.'

Jane suggested that Mary should start by sharing this with her, and so Mary continued.

Mary's anecdote   *(The letters on the paragraphs are for later reference)*

A   I asked a group of six and seven-year-olds to investigate what totals they could create from one throw of a set of three dice and the symbols +, − and =. The dice were marked with dots from one to six. They worked in pairs and had calculators and unifix cubes.

B   Two girls, Vini and Fay, used + twice (as in 3 + 2 + 6 =) and were surprised when the total stayed the same whichever order they placed the dice in. They then decided to use − . They used + first (as in 3 + 5 − 2 =) and were happy until they came up against combinations like 4 + 1 − 6 = or 2 + 1 − 5 = . To start off with, they said the answers to these were 1 and 2. Then one girl said, 'These <u>look</u> alright but I think there's something wrong.'

The conversation then went something like,

C   Nikki: 'I think the numbers are right but the order's wrong.'

Vini: 'Get the calculator and I'll do yours and you do ours. . . . .

. . . . Look what I got − 4 + 1 − 6 = −1!!'

D   Joanna had found that 2 + 1 − 5 = −2, and said, 'It won't work because you keep taking a big number from a little number.' When Fay tried to work through the number sentence using unifix cubes she said she couldn't do it, and Nikki said, 'Look. The answer is in the cubes we haven't got.' Joanna said, 'I think it (the calculator) just keeps jumping backwards.'

E   I asked them if there was anything else we could use that we made number jumps on and they went on to explore a number line. One of them said, 'You can't jump back six from five or you fall off the end!', and somebody else replied, 'If you put the zero halfway up, then it would work. 'Watch!'

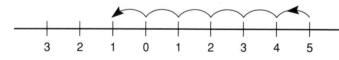

F   They were amazed to find it was true each time they tried to take a big number from a small number. Forgetting completely the original task, they set about trying out various examples and all preferred to use a number line so that they could see these 'funny numbers', as they called them. When they explained to Darren and Narinder from the same group, what they had discovered, they called them 'minus numbers' or 'take away numbers'. Vini said, 'They live before nothing and you can't see them, but they're there'. And someone else added, 'You can find if you take a big number away from a little number and they're smaller than zero.'

G   Narinder and Darren had watched carefully and were looking at their piece of paper. 'Look', said Joanna, 'You've got one!' Narinder had written 1 + 2 − 6 = 3, despite having used the calculator. He said, 'I don't want any of those! That's not what she told us to do. Can I write it like this, then it's alright?' He wrote, 3, 6 → 3, indicating the difference between 3 and 6.

H   I deliberated about whether to pursue the idea with Narinder and his partner, but left them to continue as they were.

As Mary's story unfolded, there were various interjections from Jane, having points clarified and making comments. From Jane's perspective there seemed to be a number of significant points arising from Mary's anecdote. These included:

- *the task allowed the girls to come up against notions of associativity and commutativity of addition of whole numbers (A);*

- *the lovely images which Mary seemed to convey of the pupils' perceptions of the operations involved, e.g. the calculator 'jumping backwards' or the numbers 'falling off the line' (D);*

- *the introduction of the number line, and who had actually suggested this (E);*

- *Mary's leaving Narinder and partner to continue without pushing them to consider the negative numbers (H).*

Jane recognised that the first two of these provided her, as a secondary teacher, with some unaccustomed insight into the thought processes of younger children. She recognised that more of this would be extremely valuable in understanding the mathematical backgrounds of pupils whom she met for the first time at the age of eleven or greater. However, the last two observations related strongly to concerns which were familiar to her from her own teaching. She too had been in such situations.

In discussion between the two of them it was revealed that Mary had struggled with the notion of *suggesting* the number line as a device for helping the pupils when they were trying to come to terms with the idea of negative numbers. In the event, it was the pupils themselves who had come up with the idea. Jane recalled often having been in situations when she had to decide whether to suggest something herself, or whether to allow pupils to continue with their own thinking. They both felt that this had been strongly triggered for them by the original anecdote. When *should* you actually *prod and guide* pupils?

The last sentence in the paragraph above flags an issue. When should you actually prod and guide pupils? *To express the issue clearly would need more words than these. These perhaps form a* shorthand *version of an issue, which was recognisable to the people concerned (Jane and Mary) because they coined the words in connection with their own discussion and anecdotes. Jane and Mary, in coining the words had reached a level of joint understanding so that they could talk unambiguously with a minimum of explanation. You, in reading the words, probably want to add many riders or qualifications to them. This is natural because you were not a party to the discussion which preceded the words being uttered. What is important here is that two teachers, who had in fact not talked to each other much before this meeting, and worked in different phases of education, were able to come very close in understanding issues which concerned them both. The significance here is that this had been triggered by a very brief classroom anecdote.*

FROM PAIRS TO THE WHOLE GROUP – AND SO INTO ISSUES

After about fifteen minutes the meeting between the six teachers progressed from pairs talking together to full group discussion. The group leader signalled this by asking the pairs if they were ready to share aspects of their discussion with the group as a whole. For a moment or two the pairs' discussion continued. It was followed by some shuffling as people reoriented themselves, both physically and mentally towards the next stage. There was a questioning silence as everyone worked themselves into this new phase, but no one felt ready to begin it. Jane suggested that perhaps someone would like to begin by describing something of significance which had arisen for them in consideration of one of the anecdotes.

Again there was silence, then Angie, who had been talking to Selim, broke in with a remark that she and Selim had both chosen to work on the same anecdote – anecdote number (2). Jane and Mary responded that they too had worked on this particular anecdote. Pam and Phil, the other pair, said that they had worked respectively on anecdotes (2) and (1). It was interesting that five people out of six had responded to the same anecdote. Individuals then started to say what it was that they had responded to. Discussion from this point never halted.

Pam said that what it had triggered for her was a reminder that it was better to go into an investigation *not knowing the answer*, as she was aware that if she knew any possible outcome, there was a danger of pushing pupils in a direction with which *she* was familiar but which might not be fruitful for them. She described a particular problem which she had set for some of her pupils where her own knowledge of a solution had created a tension for her when some pupils were flagging and she had to think of ways to help them. Her own solution uppermost in her mind, it had been hard to think of alternative possible suggestions.

This reminded Jane of Mary's dilemma in trying to decide whether or not she should introduce the number line as a possible way of helping her pupils. In order for her to communicate this to the others it was necessary to say something of Mary's pupils and their task. So Jane decided to try herself to put Mary's anecdote into words for the group. This was a deliberate strategy on her part to emphasise aspects of group working to others in the group who were less familiar with working in this way. She hoped that she would reinforce bonds which were already forming between herself and Mary in terms of confidence and trust. She hoped that her own ability to tell Mary's anecdote would emphasise the importance of listening carefully to what the other person had to say. She hoped to illustrate that different people put different emphases on what they hear and to hint at this by some of her comments. In the telling she pointed out some of her own reactions to the anecdote, in particular those which came from her own experience with pupils of a different age group to those described, and those which were related strongly to her own classroom experiences.

The discussion which followed hinged around the tensions between wanting to go with pupils' own ideas, and knowing what interventions to make as a teacher with wider knowledge and experience. Angie suggested that knowledge or expertise can sometimes be a barrier – it could help pupils, but it could also hinder them. Selim, referring to anecdote (3), said that it could be very threatening to teachers, however, to go into the classroom feeling inadequately prepared in terms of knowledge. However, several people recognised that teachers do have knowledge and expertise and that this cannot be removed. What is important is to develop an awareness of ways to respond to pupils when such moments of tension arise. There are important issues here for most teachers. It is likely that each teacher in the group perceived the issues differently from the others in the group, but nevertheless the use of anecdotes in expressing individual experience brought them close enough to bring concerns together and each gain from the perceptions aired.

In the space of an hour and a half many issues emerged. It was surprising how the

words of one teacher sparked off recollections of another, and in particular how the three starting anecdotes were drawn together through the discussion. They had been chosen independently for their individual potency but, as discussion proceeded, they became linked by the issues which were raised.

For example, in response to Mary's decision not to push Narinder and his partner into an overt consideration of negative numbers, Phil referred to anecdote number (1) in which the teacher had not pursued her question to Danny of 'how many more yellow ones than red ones?' He speculated that perhaps Danny was concerned with other aspects of his bead chain (such as pattern and symmetry), so that this question was, for him, quite meaningless. He recalled many situations where as a teacher he might have particular ideas in his head which were different from those of the pupil, and of the importance of trying to find out first what the pupil is thinking before plunging in with questions. Anecdote (1) had not said anything at all about the context in which Danny's work had taken place, or about the teacher's understanding of Danny's thinking. It is therefore pointless to speculate on the teacher's intentions or to suggest what she should or should not have done in the situation described. What was important here was the value of the anecdote in triggering such situations for Phil and enabling him to share these in a way to which others in the group could readily respond.

In linking Mary's response to anecdote (2) to his own response to anecdote (1), Phil was reminded of an occasion when he had been observing a probationary teacher working on speed, distance and time.

Phil's anecdote

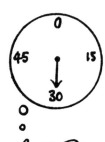

There was lots of good discussion about how far a car can travel at 60 mph in different times and how long it takes to cover different distances. The children understood and it was going quite well until the teacher formalised the discussion to

$$\text{speed} = \frac{\text{distance}}{\text{time}}.$$

Initially this went well so long as the numbers were sensible, e.g. covering 120 miles in 2 hours. But the lesson fell apart when the time was 30 minutes which the pupils could cope with mentally but they could not divide by $\frac{1}{2}$ as the inexperienced teacher expected. Hence an attainable concept was made inacessible by inappropriate generalisation.

Phil felt that the teacher had wanted to introduce the formula but had misjudged his pupils readiness for it. He said, 'As a teacher you are often pressured by wanting to *get through* a piece of work.'

REFINING THE ISSUES RAISED – AND ON TO ACTION IN THE CLASSROOM

Jane, as group leader, felt that it was important not to let the discussion end at the level of sharing anecdotes and skirting around a number of issues. She thought it important to refine issues so that it could be possible to devise appropriate responses to them in terms of classroom strategy. So, towards the end of the session she suggested that each person should spend a moment or two reflecting on the discussion so far and expressing in words one or two matters which had arisen which were important to them. As a result of doing this, it was recognised that the articulation of issues is not easy. The anecdotes had encouraged shared perceptions so that members of the group felt that they had common understanding, and awareness of issues of mutual concern. However, when it came to putting these issues into words, it was hard to find succinct ways of saying what was felt.

People struggled to say what they thought, others chipped in, and eventually a number of issues were articulated. Jane wrote them up on a board for greater permanence and group ownership. They included:

- *posing a question at the right level for a child;*

- *importance of listening to what pupils say as an indication of their thinking;*

- *recognition that a teacher's knowledge or expertise can be a barrier to helping pupils;*

- *creation of opportunities for children to communicate ideas to each other;*

- *dilemma of how to cope with ideas which pupils raise which might be conceptually too difficult for them to cope with at this stage.*

It might be argued that none of these statements is an issue. The above forms of words do, however, flag matters of concern for the participants of the group and this was what was important at this stage.

COMMENT ON THE SESSION DESCRIBED

With this crystallization or refinement of ideas, it is now possible to go one stage further and ask, 'What, as a teacher, might I do in response to the heightened awareness that this issue-raising provides?' It is possible to imagine that Jane and Mary might begin to explore the issue of when *to prod and guide pupils. They might well decide to see what happens when no guidance is given. Are pupils able to make progress or do they rapidly become frustrated and give up? As teachers they might be surprised at the resourcefulness of the pupils . . . the girls, after all, were making good progress towards considerable insight into negative numbers!*

One might also imagine how Jane and Mary would return from their classrooms with new anecdotes throwing new light on the issue under consideration . . . two professionals intimately discussing their teaching techniques with one another and actively investigating ways of improving them.

This begins to suggest an on-going side to this process of identifying issues and that is the subject of the next part of this section.

The following diagram, modified from Part IV, summarises this process.

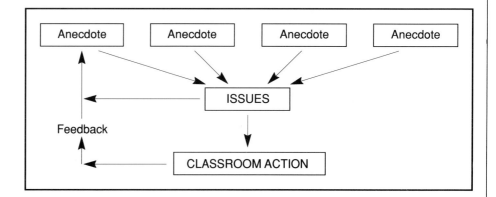

Working as a group for at least three sessions

This is an account of three consecutive sessions of one group at a conference. However, it is possible to imagine that these sessions occurred in a school, perhaps among the entire staff of a small primary school, or the members of a mathematics department in a secondary school. In a school setting there would very probably be time between the sessions for teachers to work on issues in their classrooms. This possibility is elaborated in Part V where three case studies are provided to illustrate the anecdoting process in operation in a school setting.

The account in this section shows the enormous potential of anecdotes for identifying issues on which to work in mathematics teaching. What is more, in itself it describes a way of working as a whole staff or department on improving professional teaching skills.

The initial stimuli for teachers' anecdotes in each of the three sessions vary. They range from a video excerpt, like the one mentioned in Section 1 above, and finally to the teachers' own 'stories' of brief, but significant moments that occurred in their own classrooms.

Once again it was the group leader's intervention at certain points in each session which helped the group to elicit the issues that had been raised during their discussions. Further intervention on the leader's part later caused the group to stop and identify what they were each going to do about those issues in class from that point on in time. The account, therefore gives a useful indication of the important role the group leader or chairperson has to play in the process of identifying issues to work on.

It is also interesting to note that at least three experiences of 'anecdote spawning anecdote – leading to issues for action' were required before colleagues in the group grasped the potential of the process as a way of working on improving their teaching of mathematics in class. A theoretical basis for the 'minimum of three' anecdoting experiences is given in Part VI. Sustaining the commitment of the group through the three experiences is however a vital and non-trivial task for the group leader. In this instance it took the form of alerting the group right from the start that they would only experience the full potential of the process once they had worked this way on at least three separate occasions. Sustaining the group also required constant encouragment along the way.

SESSION 1

BALL-ROLLING WITH FOUR-YEAR-OLDS – A VIDEO PRESENTATION OF AN ANECDOTE

The video extract came from a publication by the Open University, called *Working mathematically with infants* (see Part VIII). A resumé of the video excerpt and its context follows.

The ball-rolling video sequence

Mary Hamby is the teacher in the Home-School link class of rising 5-year-olds. She has been focusing on 'Cause and effect' and skills of predicting. She aimed in her teaching session to address with the children the effect of a ball rolling down a slope.

What is the effect on the distance a ball will roll starting on a slide set at different heights against a climbing frame? Can the children predict how far it will roll when the slide has a very steep gradient? And what will happen when it is 'flat'?

The children explore the distance rolled by the ball when started on the slide set at lots of different gradients. They have experimented with rolling balls down the hillock in the playground. They have rolled marbles around a dish with a piece of paint splattered paper on the base to see what pictures the rolling marbles make. All that and more, and finally Mary asks, 'If I want to make the ball roll a long way, what should I do?' After a pause for thought, Andrea announces, 'You have to put it on a high hill!'

The group of teachers watched the video. Then to get beyond initial reactions of like and dislike, they were asked by the group leader to do two things.

1. On their own and in SILENCE *to reconstruct the episode, trying to identify what they each saw.*

2. To ask questions like 'how does what I see here relate to my experiences?'

These instructions involved a conscious attempt by the group leader to provide each individual teacher with an opportunity to formulate their own view of the events in the video anecdote and then generate related anecdotes of their own before plunging into discussion with others (see 'The 1-2-4 Process' in Part III).

Next each person exchanged their view of things on the video and their related 'story' with one other member of the group. Finally the whole group came together and shared their perceptions of what had been seen. All kinds of other anecdotes from the classroom experiences of members of the group seemed to be spawned from the one 'story' presented on the video. One person told of children's attempts to predict the outcomes of varying mixes of sand, cement and water in making concrete 'strong'. Another told of pupils' predictions regarding the use of ear trumpets!

In this way the video excerpt proved to be a very potent form of anecdote, particularly as a way of starting sessions like these, and the group leader tried to ensure that people did not go off down a line of negative criticism of the teacher seen. What the sequence provided was a shared classroom experience. Everyone in the group had, in effect, seen the same event taking place in a classroom and so were all in a position to tell a 'story' and talk about it. Where there were disagreements about what had happened, it was possible to go back and review the tape.

Discussion was very vigorous. One teacher declared,

> *'I found myself really identifying with that teacher. When I teach a small group like that I tend to talk too much; I don't wait quite long enough to let the children do their thinking before I cut in.'*

Another teacher in the group expressed doubts about the way in which she taught. She said,

> *'Mary pushed her planned objectives . . . but then I recognise that in my own teaching. Perhaps I should allow more time for the children to discuss what they saw and to listen to one another, building new ideas from what other people say.'*

All the while, the group leader was trying to tease out or abstract the issues that lay behind what people were saying. The nature and timing of teacher intervention in the learning process was one sameness that seemed to run through all the anecdotes. This 'abstractor' role, often unvoiced, was nevertheless crucial to the group leader's subsequent chairing of the group's discussion.

After twenty minutes or so the group leader intervened:

> *'I wonder if we might move on to a slightly different phase. Just pause and think about the issues that have come to the surface as we've talked . . . let's just do that for a moment. See if we can jot down issues in learning and teaching which seem to lie behind the stories that we've all been discussing . . . Do this on our own first, then we'll share.'*

Everyone wrote furiously in their note book. Then, when they went 'public', the group leader put their ideas about issues up on a flipchart. These were some of the items offered.

- *The issue of how much a teacher ought to intervene and the nature of that intervention – to lead the child further in their own thinking or to focus their attention . . . or to find the answer the teacher wants!?*

- *Which is the important thing in a lesson – should we be concentrating on how the child is learning or on how we are teaching? Was today a valuable experience for the children in my class?*

- *Is there a place for mixed styles of teaching? Is it wrong to ask closed questions; is it wrong to present teacher-directed work?*

- *Do I give children time enough to think things through for themselves – and when do I intervene to help?*

- *A similar question relating to development of the language to talk about their observations.*

- *There is a real need to create time to discuss things with pupils – time to listen and time to talk things through – how can I do this?*

- *As teachers, we tend to push for the achievement of planned objectives on some scheme – but ought we to pull back from these in order to establish sound discussion skills first . . . and what is the effect on pupils' learning if they do learn to get ideas from peers? Do they learn to modify their conjectures as a result of listening to others; do they learn to evaluate one another's responses and make suggestions for improvements?*

- *Getting children to do the thinking. Using questions like, 'Alex, where will you put the slide to make the ball go fast?' 'What do you think will happen when we put the slide right down here?'*

- *Getting children to make sense of their play experience – the children bringing all their experiences together to formulate some sort of conclusions . . . when should teachers intervene to do this . . . if at all?*

A crucial stage had now been reached. So far all that could be said was that a group of teachers had had a fairly high level discussion about a range of issues in the teaching and learning of mathematics. Unless there was a disciplined attempt on the part of the group to decide upon just one issue to work on and then identify a specific action to try out in class 'tomorrow', little of professional value might take place, beyond an increased awareness of the issues raised.

Having therefore, identified a whole collection of issues, the group leader intervened once more to try and take the group this one stage further. Here is what one teacher decided to do.

> *'I think holding back to give children time to think things through is something I really need to work on so I'm going to try asking some of those "what-do-you-think, Alex?" type of questions and then forcing myself to say nothing for at least two minutes . . . I want to see what happens.'*

This is indicative of the kind of 'actions' teachers decided to take. What could be a better start into addressing the issue of when and how to intervene in class? One can certainly envisage teachers coming back with an entirely new set of anecdotes of their own which, in turn would give rise to further discussion amongst colleagues and the subsequent 'action' in their maths lessons. Right at the end, the group leader drew attention to the process that was underway, saying,

> *'Before we go, just let me leave you with this thought . . . from just one anecdote, a whole collection of thoughts on teaching and teaching styles in mathematics have been brought to the surface. Furthermore we leave, having decided as a staff to work on one of these issues in very specific ways and then come back with our own stories of what happened. In this way we will become a group who talk much more about ways and means of teaching mathematics.'*

At the conference it was not possible to take such action before the next session. However, in a school this would not only be possible, but natural to the way of making progress.

SESSION 2

A WRITTEN ANECDOTE PROVIDES THE STIMULUS THIS TIME

At the start of this second session, the group had at last an inkling of what 'anecdoting' was about, and were also more confident in talking to each other. The three written anecdotes provided were the same as those used by Jane's group as described in section 2 above. The one that spawned most anecdotes about people's experiences in maths lesson was *Panic*.

Panic

I've never taught this topic before, and I'm not very confident about it. I prepared myself thoroughly by reading a number of books, but I couldn't bring myself to make it as open-ended as I usually do. I taught it very straight from the blackboard and didn't really invite questions. When Elizabeth asked a question that I didn't know the answer to I nearly panicked. But I was able to invite the rest of the class to comment on the question, and Nelista said something that I realised was right and so I took it from there and it was OK.

One teacher, René, responded with the following anecdote.

René's anecdote

. . . very early in my career I was really put on the spot by a pupil. Although I had a degree in maths I still didn't have any sound number bond facts. I still used to count on my fingers . . . you know behind my back or under the table. For some reason we needed to know the answer to 6 and 7. Before I could reach for my fingers, one child called out 13! I was completely nonplussed. In self-defence, I suppose, I spun round and said, 'How did you get that!? . . . so quickly too!' Almost wondering what the problem was the pupil said, 'Well, it's easy. I thought of two 6s and one more!' I was amazed. Still reeling from that, I asked, 'How did others do that?' All sorts of ideas came at me . . . 'Well I thought of it as one less than 2 sevens.' . . . 'I saw the seven split up into 4 and 3, then I knew the six needed four to make it up to 10, so it's 13' . . . It was a new world to me. Suddenly for the first time in my life I was being shown by my own pupils all sorts of ways of combining numbers. I came to see that I'd, in fact, stumbled on a highly effective teaching approach in maths which I've used ever since . . . I'm never afraid to admit I don't know something and the pupils are always so willing to help me. That's tremendous for them and really helps their own understanding to be able to teach me!'

Once again, at the intervention of the group leader, the teachers went beyond the level of anecdote and identified the issue of:

> 'changing from being an answer-orientated, teacher knows all the answers, kind of teacher to one at ease about being able to learn from the pupils themselves.'

Subsequent encouragement from the group leader to identify 'actions' we'd try in class next Monday, led several teachers to:

> '. . . ask, on at least 3 occasions in class, "How did you get your answer?" and then note down what was learned from each pupil as a result.'

Clearly the potential of anecdotes for generating a range of new but related anecdotes and subsequent reflection on one's teaching approaches was tremendous. The teachers were beginning to see the power of anecdote to raise issues that could be worked on in class. Just as the '6 + 7 = 13' teacher had learned of many new things to try out as a result of sharing his difficulty with his pupils, so also teachers learn of other responses to situations in maths lessons by sharing their experiences in class with their colleagues. As the teacher above had begun to experiment with a 'teacher as co-learner with the pupils' approach, so here, at the level of teacher-development, was a 'teacher as co-learner with one's colleagues' process beginning to emerge.

THE BEST ANECDOTE OF ALL TO STIMULATE DISCUSSION AND TRIAL OF NEW IDEAS – ONE'S OWN

By now the group of teachers were becoming quite enthusiastic about the value of anecdotes as a basis for working together on teaching approaches in mathematics.

This growing enthusiasm was due in large measure to the way in which the group leader, occasionally, had drawn the teachers' attention to the way in which the original anecdote had only been a starting point in the process of raising issues about teaching. Becoming more aware of the process, the teachers were now willing to invest their energies in sharing some anecdotes of their own without initial stimulus.

Alison's anecdote

Recently my class visited the fairground. When we returned we decided to make some hand-held windmills like those they'd seen on sale. Jonathon, normally a low achiever, just seemed to click on to the rotating symmetry and successfully made one where everyone else failed. He felt so pleased with himself, especially when the others all asked him to help them. He also went on to make the only helter-skelter that worked! He's grown in confidence ever since!!

Liam's anecdote

That reminds me of two boys in my class, twins . . . one was always very quiet, preferring people to 'go and ask my brother!' He had no expectations about his ability to do anything at all! We were exploring sharing and we needed to share one between two. Nobody could do it, but then this quiet lad came out with an idea of how to do it which worked. His self-confidence also grew and now his achievement all round has improved from a year ago! I can pinpoint the change to this event.

Madeline's anecdote

I had a child like that – his older brother always made him feel so inadequate until one day we were using multilink to find how many shapes could be made with just 5 cubes. This lad had a special success and his whole progress has changed.

Sajid's anecdote

```
I've an instance which is kind of the opposite way round. Joanna is a
very able girl, with a nasty way of telling others when they're wrong
. . . 'Look, Sir, she's done it wrong, she should have done it like
this . . .' Not surprisingly Joanna was becoming very unpopular
amongst her peers. We're in a small two teacher school and Joanna's
manner changed when, one day, she was asked to look after the little
ones in the class. For once instead of being critical she was
helpful.
```

It was as if something in each anecdote was sparking off a memory of a similar situation in the recent, but vivid past experiences of other teachers in the group. Without the intervention that followed this might have been nothing more than a glorified story-telling session. The group leader asked, 'Is there any theme running through each of these anecdotes? Let's just consider that for a moment.'

After a few moments thought, it was Alison who announced, 'Yes there is, it's all about self-esteem. Joanna has no esteem for anyone else and everyone is getting browned off. Your twin, Liam, had a low self-opinion of himself and learned differently . . . I think it's all about building confidence, building a history of success . . . and a child's whole self-image changing as a result.'

Further discussion sharpened this issue up a bit more then the group leader pressed the challenge still further. 'Well then, of all the ideas we've discussed what will you each take away and work on in your classrooms tomorrow?' The intention was for each person to define an attainable target connected with building histories of success.

At least six targets were set within the group. One in particular stands out; Joanna's teacher, Sajid, declared:

'Joanna . . . very able, but attracts such adverse attention because she's always pointing out the mistakes of her classmates . . . a clever clogs of the worst kind! That discussion about building up a history of success inspires me to have a chat with Joanna suggesting that instead of putting her peers down she actively look for something that is said or done that is right and make that a basis for discussion. I will watch out for evidence of this new positive behaviour and praise both Joanna for using it and the other pupil for entering into the dialogue with Joanna to build a clearer understanding. This should build histories of success all round . . . You know, I can see a real chance of changing the whole atmosphere in my class by doing this; till now Joanna has been causing relationships to go rapidly from bad to worse!'

Apart from changing the tide of opinion against Joanna this option of Sajid's was positively fostering pupil-pupil discussion in the class . . . a cherished Cockcroft 243[1] objective for teaching mathematics.

Once again you can well imagine what might have happened when Sajid reported back to the group about Joanna's progress. We don't, unfortunately have that feedback but you can see how this would amount, in effect, to new anecdotes leading to sustained discussion about the issues involved and further activity in the classroom. In this way the staff would continuously be sharing accounts of events taking place in their classrooms and supporting one another in attempts to improve their professional practice as a whole.

---

1 DES, 1982 (see Part VIII).

SOME CONCLUDING REMARKS

It takes time to appreciate the value of the anecdoting process. It seems that a sequence of three sessions is a necessary minimum for a group to establish the potential of the processes for identifying issues to work on in the classroom and, as indicated earlier, Part VI explains why this might be so.

As a way of working for a whole staff in a primary school or department in a secondary school one can detect an internal consistency of approach to the professional development by teachers with investigative approaches to teaching pupils. Just as in an investigative approach pupils are encouraged to formulate concepts as a result of their activity and exchange of ideas with peers, so also does this approach require the teachers to identify the issues, do things in their classrooms and discuss the outcomes in order to arrive at new perceptions of learning and teaching in their professional situations . . . it's a case of 'do as you would be done by'!

One may usefully impose the INSET infrastructure, to be found in INSET days or Day Closures and Directed or Planned Activity time, on this notion of a three-session minimum:

For example, during an INSET day or Day Closure the whole department/school might carry out anecdoting sessions such as the video or printed story sessions above. The group could end with an undertaking to go away and work in their classrooms on the issues they identified.

A further undertaking would be for teachers to note down brief but vivid accounts of events in their classrooms related to those issues, to share with colleagues when they all convene at an agreed date for an hour of so of directed activity time.

In the first directed activity hour the school/department could meet to share their own anecdotes from their recent classroom activity on the issues identified on the earlier INSET day or Day Closure. This is, in effect, a session such as the third described above. Once again, ideas would be shaped and issues redefined leading to further classroom work and repeats of this particular directed or planned activity hour.

In effect this becomes a way of actively exploring the teaching and learning processes within the classrooms of a school or department as a group of teachers – a way of working on one's own professional development.

Part V takes up these ideas, describing case studies from a school in which teachers actively worked together in a way similar to that described here. It also suggests how you might begin such sessions with colleagues.

The next part of this section looks at some of the questions which an anecdoting approach can raise, presented through the reflections of the group leaders of two particular sessions at a conference.

4

Anecdoting from a cold beginning

▓ *In the previous section we saw particular examples of how the anecdoting process can develop as a group of teachers grows more confident in this way of working. The 'warmth' needed to encourage this development can, perhaps, be more easily generated when the teachers concerned either know one another initially or have the chance of becoming familiar with each other through several sessions of a course.*

Nevertheless, there may be times when, for a variety of reasons, a group finds difficulty 'getting going'; when anecdotes fail to flow spontaneously and the session seems in danger of floundering.

The two accounts which follow are instances of just such a situation. Each is given by the group leader of a particular session. They reveal many common features but each has a different emphasis. In the first account the opening minutes look less than promising; no-one seems prepared to make the first move. The remarkable factor is that once something has been offered, however unlikely, the group is somehow empowered to engage in a far-reaching discussion in which issues fundamental to classroom practice emerge. The second account highlights the value of a thoughtfully planned structure (in this case the '1–2–4' approach described in Part III), which provides the framework for the fruitful exchange of experiences and ideas. It also emphasises the importance of the three sessions in building confidence and skill in this way of working.

1. A TALE OF THE UNEXPECTED

At the beginning of a group session at a teachers' conference participants had been invited to offer their own anecdotes (as in session 3 in the previous section). They had already had a limited experience of the 'anecdoting process' in earlier sessions when they had worked on prepared anecdotes in the form of video and written material. However, the group involved in this account, which included teachers from all phases, was reluctant to offer any anecdote themselves. In fact, the offering of anecdotes from cold without immediate stimulation or forethought was felt to be potentially difficult.

▓ *We may ask why? Is it that we genuinely have none in our consciousness at that time? Or are we confused by the lack of indications as to what may be relevant, interesting, engaging . . . when confronted with a clean slate? Are there other reasons?*

After an uncomfortable silence the following anecdote was tentatively offered.

Football

I love football although I have never been able to play it that well. Every Sunday morning I play for a team. All the others are better than me — and we are an extremely mixed-ability bunch. I learn a hell of a lot by playing with those who are better than me **and** I enjoy trying to improve.

What follows is an attempt to sketch the subsequent discussion, largely through verbatim comments and questions of the six members of the group and the group leader. All comments are on the thoughts triggered by the initial telling, i.e. on the anecdote itself – rather than on the process of working and reflecting together in this way.

There was a brief period of two minutes individual reflection, leading to a sharing of responses in pairs and subsequently as a whole group discussion.

THE WHOLE GROUP SHARING

One teacher commented,

'We looked at each other in amazement – but having had the two minutes we did focus on what we considered . . . it worked as a trigger . . . but to work on an easier task . . . generating our own anecdotes . . . something completely different!'

An issue seemed to be

'. . . a weak player, enjoying and valuing the company of better players . . .'

There followed some discussion about the arrangements in one school where the bottom six pupils in mathematics were taken out, with nine others who had some problems, so they could work with two teachers. What happens to pupil expectations; how do they express them in respect of their capacity to do mathematics?

'. . . divisions/groupings influence the expectations of pupils';

'. . . the higher band gets the cream of the teachers';

'Do we create situations where the youngsters are not allowed to play . . . ?'

'Life makes strong demands on knowing where you are at!'

'. . . the need to accept small failures with small successes'.

'In constraining opportunities, . . . this leads to the notion that this is as far as a youngster can get . . .'

'Do you ever feel that you are letting your team mates down? . . . there is not necessarily the same feeling in a mathematics class.'

'You cannot have a good teacher without a good class and you cannot have a good class without a good teacher.'

'Everyone lets the side down sometimes.'

At this point a small example was given by one of the group, of an awkward pupil in one class who influences every lesson.

'. . . is it about the relationship with the teacher or the relationship with mathematics and fellow pupils?'

'Opportunities should not be diminished if they are spurned – the level of response should not determine the extent of the opportunity . . . but what about the requirements of other subject areas which may specify levels of attainment in mathematics?'

Some discussion followed about teaching styles.

> '. . . the more powerful way of managing the learning is by stepping back and asking the right sort of questions';
>
> 'How comfortable are we with the teacher's role as one of "leading from behind"?'
>
> 'Within the setted group there is a barrier between teacher and pupil. I can't talk to them. It's my own observation of my own teaching . . . an assumption that they are all working at their own level . . . but with mixed ability teaching I have an overwhelming feeling of children re-inventing the wheel!'

The group leader summed up at the end.

> 'There was a reference to go and get a book if you are stuck, raising wider questions of resources for learning, the organisation of the classroom, expected behaviours and the effect of teacher intervention – who or what does the pupil turn to if a problem is recognised . . . what is the climate for learning?'

 The power of this account extends well beyond the pure recounting of a particular experience or example. It demands that we consider:

- *in what sense can we anticipate the effect of an anecdote told for a pre-determined purpose?*

- *in what circumstance should a group leader intervene to guide the course of discussion?*

2. 1-2-GO!

This session was again the third of three in which anecdotes were being presented in different ways. The same participants were working together and several spoke of their relief that they were with people they had already met rather than with a new group. They appreciated the trust and warmth that had been engendered in the group already which helped in this task, the most difficult to date, telling their own anecdote.

In spite of the confidence that familiarity with fellow group members had built up, participants found it difficult to think of a suitable anecdote and, after about fifteen or twenty minutes, only three of six had chosen an anecdote to tell. The group leader therefore paired them for pair-sharing so that each pair had a member with an anecdote to tell.

Interchange between the pairs soon began and in a few minutes two out of the three pairs had exchanged anecdotes – a demonstration of the power of an anecdote to generate others in response.

The group now shared as a whole group (structure 1-2-6 in this case – see Part III). Issues were quickly identified and the discussion dwelt on those issues for about half an hour after which a further period of silent reflection ensued.

This time anecdotes emerged without any difficulty within the whole group. All participants were able to produce new anecdotes which both related to the issues previously identified and brought up new issues for discussion. The group became extremely enthusiastic, feeling that it would be useful to make a record of the anecdotes and the issues they exemplified. They were particularly interested to find that, although each group of anecdotes centred on its own particular issues, it was often possible to see links with other anecdotes and issues as discussion developed.

At the end of the session all were agreed that the quality of the discussion had been higher, and that a greater depth of perception had been achieved in this session than had been the case in the earlier sessions. They spoke of the sense of a build-up through the three different sessions (video, written, self-generated) and a feeling that without the earlier sessions they would not have achieved so much.

Subsequently, the group leader pondered on the way in which a session with initial difficulties could develop into discussion of such high quality. What were the factors that led to this being the case? What place did anecdotes themselves take in the generation of an ability to interrelate and to articulate anecdotes of sufficient power to elicit issues? How much did the 1-2-6 structure contribute and how much depended upon the greater confidence which had been built up through returning to a familiar group? What part did other intervening groupings play in this sense of 'coming home' to an environment which could succour the exchange of ideas through anecdotes?

You may like to reflect on these two accounts – and on the questions they raise – in the light of the quite strong advice which was given with regard to group leader involvement in the first three parts of this section.

We should like to re-emphasise the value of making up your own mind about the most appropriate ways of handling or organising sessions.

You may like to read Parts V, VI and VII in which the school-based inservice event is considered in much more detail and a model is proposed through which such events may become a powerful basis for professional development.

THE GROUP

Part III introduces aspects of group working which are fundamental to the approach described in Part IV. This includes a structured approach to group discussion, consideration of how groups can work together, and the role of group leader.

Contents

Introduction

1. The 1-2-4 process

2. The nature and purpose of a group and the role of group leader

3. Lessons of a weekend conference – a group leader's reaction to criticism.

   Interlude   Perception – from *seeing* to *interpreting*

4. Some starters for group discussion

5. Weekend diary of a group leader

   Postlude   Perceptions of participants

Introduction

The way of working which forms a basis for all the sessions described in Part II, and for the anecdoting process described in Part IV, depends essentially on the nature of *the teacher group*.

It is very difficult for any teacher actively to develop classroom approaches alone. Quite apart from the external pressures which make this difficult, solitary professional development is extremely hard to sustain.

The teacher group can provide a mutually supportive structure in which development can take place. The group meetings provide a forum for sharing and discussion, from which individuals can undertake action in their classrooms, and to which they can bring their questions and concerns.

Part III addresses a variety of issues related to working as a group. There are many sources where such issues have been tackled (some of which are referred to), but it is the intention here only to address group structures as they relate to the anecdoting process and its associated way of working. The nature of the group in terms of support and trust, and mutual sharing, is important to the anecdoting process which depends on participants being willing to share personal concerns and rely on these being treated with respect. The group must be willing to undertake a quite disciplined approach to discussion and issue raising, and it is important that at least one person in the group should be alert to this. Part III thus suggests how these aspects might be achieved.

It is recognised that, initially at least, any group needs a group leader who is familiar with the anecdoting process and is prepared to act as guide to the group in establishing the process. This is not to suggest that the leader would in any way control the thinking of the group, but rather would act as a focusing agent, reminding the group of the different stages of the process. The role of group leader is therefore discussed in some detail.

In order for discussion and anecdoting to begin, some stimulus is needed to encourage thinking and raise the warmth within a group. A number of potential starters for group discussion are offered. The perceptions of the participants of a group can influence strongly the direction of discussion, and the focus on particular issues. An interlude suggests some features of perception, particularly with respect to certain starting points, and we include also a postlude which includes perceptions of teachers who have taken part in the anecdoting process.

A key feature of Part III is the 'Weekend diary of a group leader', in section 5 below. This provides insight into the thinking and concerns of one person who acted as group leader at one of the weekend conferences at which the anecdoting process was trialled (see Appendix). It is valuable reading for anyone who contemplates setting up a group or undertaking the role of group leader.

Part III begins with an introduction to a process for group working which we have called the 1-2-4 process. This has been found to be very effective in drawing group participants into thinking and discussion. Its form may be modified according to the particular nature of any group, but the structure is one which we strongly recommend.

The 1-2-4 Process

A structured approach to discussion

Many of the group sessions described in this pack have been purposely structured in the following way

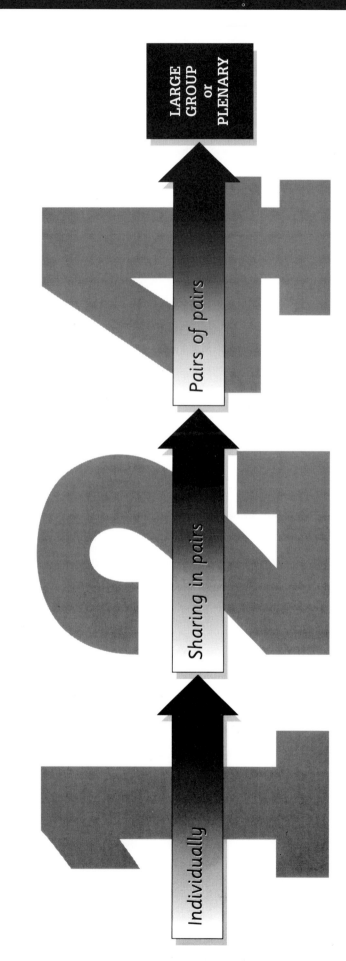

Individually

Sharing in pairs

Pairs of pairs

LARGE GROUP or PLENARY

This approach can be helpful for differing reasons at each of these levels as the following pages show.

1

Reminds each participant that they have their own points to make

Fixing own images/ideas before taking account of others'

Individually

Helps to focus on the overall purpose of the discussion

Many participants can be nervous of speaking in large groups and will be careful to conceal views on which they may be attacked; others, whilst waiting, may lose confidence to contribute.

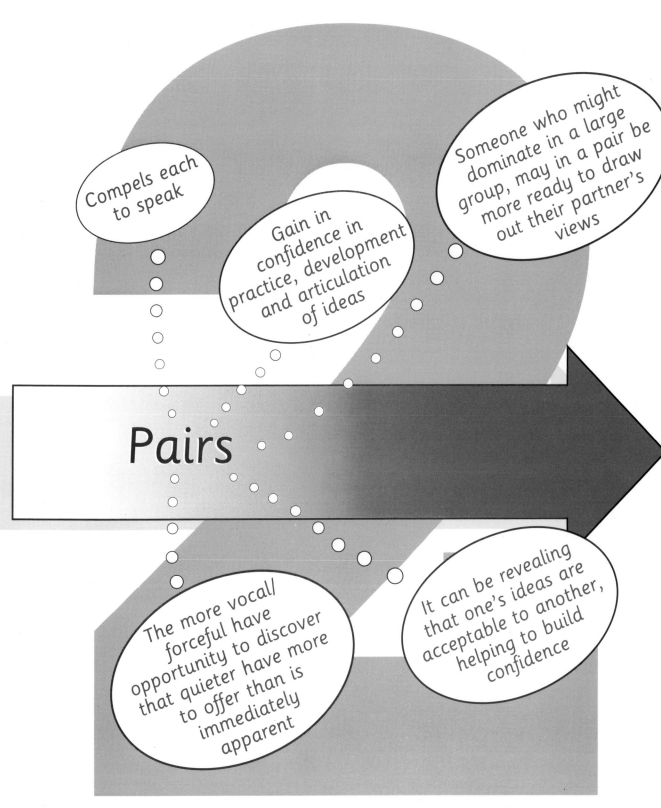

Involves everybody from the start, creating an air of activity and exchange of ideas rather than awkward silence.

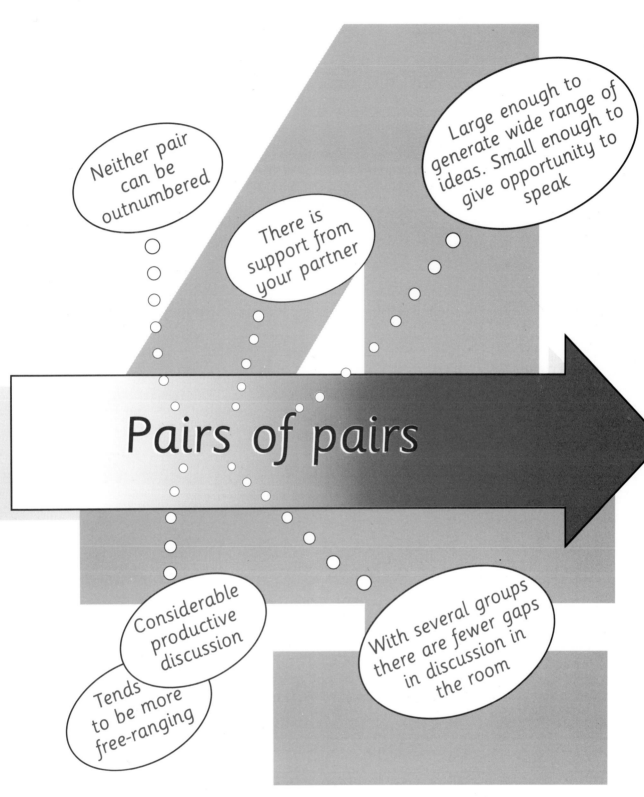

Working towards a genuine whole group *sharing* rather than just the unrelated swapping of individual views.

LARGE GROUP or PLENARY

Fosters cohesiveness with the whole group

Gives a purpose to earlier discussion

Allows insight into aspects which smaller groups may have left unexplored

Although perhaps not everyone speaks, the non-speakers can feel their views are represented by others from their small group

The nature and purpose of a group and the role of a group leader

When an anecdote is recounted, many possible meanings can emerge, some seemingly superficial, others more deeply embedded, and all individual to the listener. Perhaps most can be made of such potential diversity by sharing meanings in some structured manner within a group, so that individuals can benefit from the perceptions of others. To do this *effectively*, careful thought needs to be given to what it is that characterises effective group work, and especially to the potentially vital role of the group leader in encouraging a *fruitful* climate for group discussion.

There are many sources of thinking and reflection on groups and group work. We shall not try to be either detailed or comprehensive in referring to these, but rather supply a few references which may be of help to a group leader or convenor.

WHAT IS A GROUP?

An early definition by Hare (1962)[1] gave us:

'There are . . . characteristics which distinguish a group from a collection of individuals.'

- *The members of a group are interactive with one another.*

- *They share a common goal and set of norms which give direction and limits to their activity.*

- *They also develop a set of roles and a network of interpersonal attraction which serves to differentiate them from other groups.*

It seems apparent that for effectiveness, the experience of working together needs to recognise the opportunities to build up some of these characteristics.

AWARENESS

Gattengo (1974) said:

. . . only awareness is educable.'

The opportunity exists, in group work, for the sharing and refinement of awareness. This requires insight into the role of the group. One role of the group leader is to work with the sometimes uncomfortable issues behind what is being spoken about.

To take part in exchanges implies the creation of situations where there is an element of *risk* for the group, and for individuals within the group. For the individual it may be the challenge to ideas held, despite knowing beforehand what is to be scrutinised. However, sometimes the risk lies in the lack of prior knowledge, and in the consequent challenge to what was thought to be unassailable.

Initially the trigger anecdote for reflection will lead to an artificial situation. As Sturgess (1988) pointed out, levels of risk and anxiety are set up in a laboratory situation:

'. . . but once the initial artificial steps have been taken, and the participants begin to respond with the senses, emotions and intellect, then the whole experience becomes 'real' and rich in potential for learning.'

---

1 See Part VIII to follow up references.

1-2-4

....

The GROUP LEADER can add to
the sense of progress by making notes
of points, mentally or, preferably, in
writing, or by asking for brief summaries
of input from constituent groups on
a flipchart or O.H.P.

In open plenary taking one point at a
time; only entering a point which is
accepted by <u>all</u> members of the group
are two examples which could be
further explored. The latter is valuable
for distilling the keywords or headlines
relating to an area which has hitherto
been ill-defined.

(Easen 1985)

LEADERSHIP STYLES

Experiential and participatory learning is often interpreted as implying a lack of structure. In fact the opposite is the case. For progress to be made and recognised, there must be a clear and well-organised structure. This structure must be explicit and understood to some degree by all participants. Crucially the responsibility for this lies with a group leader. Certain factors can be identified as contributing to effective group leadership, for example:

- *basic listening skills;*

- *the capacity to use specific examples;*

- *the capacity to act honestly within a position of trust invested by the group members;*

- *the capacity to communicate respect for ideas and individuals;*

- *the capacity to communicate understanding of group and individual feeling;*

- *the capacity to keep the risk level acceptable for each individual member;*

- *competence and knowledge of the forms of the work of the group;*

- *knowledge of and confidence to use, a range of methods to optimise the skills and experiences of the group;*

- *working knowledge of group theory and practical experience of using this theory;*

- *ability to help participants to relate group learning and experience to work in other contexts.*

If you are interested in following some of these points further, you could refer to the work of Satow and Evans (1983) for an accessible introduction to activities relating to maximising the effectivensss of group working methods.

What follows are some thoughts on the role of group leadership related to our experience of sharing and working on anecdotes.

WORKING ON ANECDOTES – THE GROUP LEADER'S ROLE

1. *To make the environment 'safe' to participants. To endeavour to keep the 'risk' factor at a manageable level, being prepared to encounter the unexpected.*

2. *To get discussion going. To encourage all members of the group to take part, possibly through the 1-2-4 process.*

3. *Possibly to take part in the discussion. Care must be taken here as to how this is seen. For example it may be* intended *as a genuine contribution, to take its place alongside those from other contributors, but might be seen as a form of direction, as* the way that the leader thinks the discussion should go.

4. *To encourage reflection on the discussion. To raise awareness of the participants of what it is that they are participating in.*

5. *To maintain, mentally, an overview of what is taking place and to be prepared to summarise and to focus attention of participants where this seems appropriate – perhaps drawing participants' attention to stages of the anecdoting process or encouraging the group to avoid 'just rambling'.*

The leader must be sensitive to the fact that anything which she says will be interpreted in terms of its coming from the group *leader*. Hence it is difficult to offer any contribution neutrally. The more experienced the group become in working together and what this involves, the easier it will be for the group leader to take a more participative role.

3 Steps in Disciplined Intervention

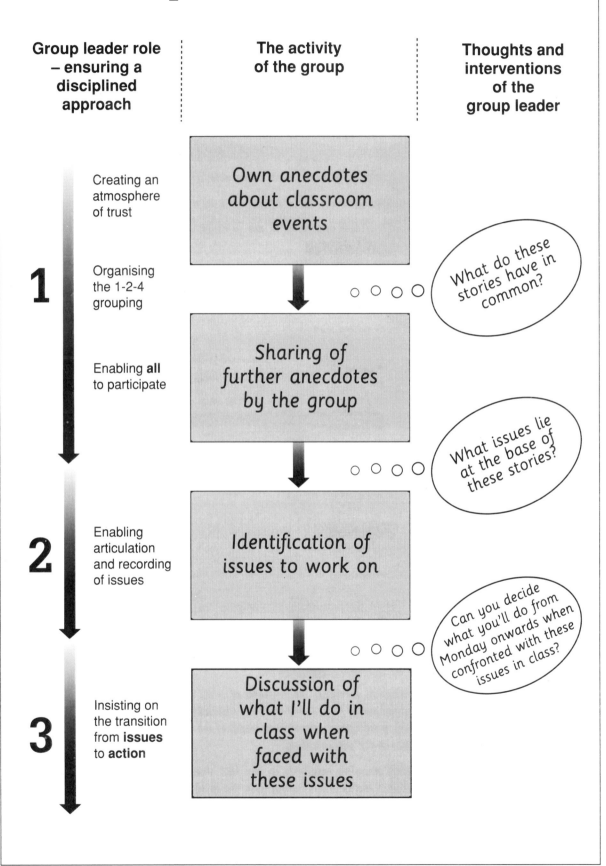

Group leader role – ensuring a disciplined approach

The activity of the group

Thoughts and interventions of the group leader

1

Creating an atmosphere of trust

Organising the 1-2-4 grouping

Enabling **all** to participate

2

Enabling articulation and recording of issues

3

Insisting on the transition from **issues** to **action**

Own anecdotes about classroom events

What do these stories have in common?

Sharing of further anecdotes by the group

What issues lie at the base of these stories?

Identification of issues to work on

Can you decide what you'll do from Monday onwards when confronted with these issues in class?

Discussion of what I'll do in class when faced with these issues

In promoting the anecdoting process a major task of the group leader is that of encouraging the group to reflect on their anecdotes to allow the issues to become more explicit. It is all too easy for the group to dwell in the anecdotes and never really move beyond this stage. A considerable degree of group discipline is required to make the issues explicit. In the early days of working as a group it will probably be up to the group leader to focus the group's attention on issues and encourage them to articulate what they see the issues as being. It may be necessary for the group leader to give an example of what she sees as the issues behind certain anecdotes. However, it is also important to help members start to express issues themselves and a delicate balance is involved where the group leader is concerned between providing examples and doing all the work.

The diagram on the facing page shows steps in the anecdoting process and indicates aspects of the group leader's role relative to these. On the left are aspects of this role which contribute to a disciplined approach to the anecdoting process and on the right are some of the thoughts or questions which might be asked. Intervention by the group leader may be seen in terms of three steps, the first of which involves establishing atmosphere and organising what people do; the second involves helping the group to extract issues and the third involves ensuring some movement towards deciding on possible classroom action. These steps of the anecdoting process are discussed in more detail in Part IV. See also Part II for examples of the group leader's action in practical situations and of questions which this raises.

One strategy for the group leader is to play the role of scribe at the board, writing up the words of group members in expressing an issue. Once some words have been written, and they are seen to be quite ordinary, then it is more likely that others will join in offering other contributions. A barrier to be overcome is that often people are too shy initially to offer words because they do not sound well polished. If it can be seen that once the words are out, then the group can work on them, it is likely that more words will come. However, it must be remembered that writing gives power, and this is a danger to which the group leader needs to be sensitive.

In professional development sessions where development of the anecdoting process is not the main focus of the session, but where it might nevertheless be of use, there are two major requirements of the group leader.

The first is *being aware*. When you have worked in this way often, and are convinced of its potential, then it is likely to come to mind readily when a situation arises which could benefit from it. You can then find an opportunity to set it in motion (see Part VII for examples of this).

The second requirement is to have some confidence in the process, perhaps because you *are* convinced of its potential, so that you can introduce it with confidence evident in your voice and action. This helps others to believe that what they are being asked to do is likely to be productive, and therefore to take part positively.

The message here is that you do not necessarily need to plan a session in terms of anecdoting, but simply to be aware of the anecdoting process so that if an opportunity arises, you can suggest an appropriate activity. This avoids the slightly artificial nature of some starts to sessions in which participants are not yet familiar with the process and find it difficult to perceive the reasons behind what they are being asked to do.

It is also true, that once a group becomes used to working together and familiar with the use of anecdotes to raise issues, that an anecdoting mode can be engaged without any overt move to instigate it. It becomes a quite natural part of working together.

GUIDELINES FOR LEADING INSET GROUPS

We conclude this section of Part III by reproducing some guidelines for leading INSET groups from a Bedfordshire manual for implementing the National Curriculum Key Stage 3 in Mathematics.[1] Some of these may be relevant to your particular circumstances, or to the particular issues or concerns you wish to address.

- *For each session or group of sessions set yourself clear and realistic objectives and communicate them to all participants.*

- *Make clear decisions about the resources required, and the principal support for any presentations to be made, i.e. OHP, flipcharts, handouts, etc.*

- *How will you divide the total time available into manageable chunks?*

- *Make prior arrangements for refreshment breaks.*

- *Perhaps you can identify other colleagues who can help to lead sessions? Using several colleagues adds variety but does require clear and mutual understanding of the part each is to play in the overall plan for the session(s).*

- *Think carefully about how you wish to encourage active participation:*
  - *at what point will you wish to break into smaller groups?*
  - *what is a sensible size for each of these sub-groups?*
  - *what will be your role during small group work?*
  - *are you looking for an oral or written response from each of the smaller groups?*
  - *in the event of oral responses will you exhaust the comments of one group before taking those of the next – or will you permit just one key point per group or what . . . ?*
  - *to give opportunity for everybody to contribute when set a task it is invariably of value to encourage individual (silent) reflection before small group discussion.*

- *If you are asking colleagues to make value decisions it is likely that conflict will arise. It is important to concentrate on resolving differences apparent through the ideas expressed – rather than those due to purpose, style and personality.*

- *Listen, and respond or intercede carefully, to what is being said.*

- *Observe how colleagues are working together.*

- *How can you ensure that decisions made by the group are kept by the group?*

- *Before each session have some notion of the criteria you will use to evaluate its effectiveness.*

---

1 See Part VIII.

Lessons of a weekend conference – a group leader's reaction to criticism

■ *In the preface we explained that the ideas and processes suggested in this publication were trialled at two weekend conferences. Building on the experience gained from the first of these conferences we felt able to pursue our research in greater depth at the second. We were keen to explore the use of anecdoting to identify issues of common concern to teachers and then to move one step further so that examination of these concerns had an effect on future classroom practice.*

As a co-organiser and group leader I was especially interested to see how the participants received the programme and how they reacted within the groups. We had made a conscious decision not to explain the process to the participants at the start of the weekend but to allow them to experience this way of working without preconceptions. They were grouped in two ways: A-groups were same-phase and B-groups were cross-phase. Each teacher was in one A and one B group and these alternated between sessions.

The comments I received during the conference and read subsequently on the evaluation sheets provided much food for thought. A great deal of the comment was encouraging, positive and enthusiastic but I was particularly struck by the reactions of three of the teachers. I feel that their comments can be used to stimulate reflection on some of the more difficult aspects of running such a conference, or of working in this way in a school setting.

A description of how the conferences were organised is provided in the Appendix at the end of the pack. Reference to this may be useful in putting the following writing into context.

THE CRITICISM

Rashid

Rashid's worries emerged following a talk on the way in which anecdotes can be used to raise warmth, to identify issues and to foster an atmosphere of support and co-operation amongst teachers, thereby creating a climate for classroom change.

As soon as the session broke up into cross-phase groups he said he was concerned that the conference was presenting too rosy a picture of the possibilities arising from working with anecdotes; that the picture it was giving of teaching was too limited and that there were corresponding negatives attached to the way of working that were not being brought out.

Moreover, he felt that anecdotes were capable of different interpretations; they might be used to justify unacceptable as well as good practice and that they might not take sufficient account of differing perceptions.

He was particularly critical of the lack of sufficient input from the organisers. He said that no teacher would expect children to operate lesson after lesson without input from the teacher and that adults too required input. Layer upon layer of the same thing, in this case discussion through and about anecdotes, could obscure the real issues.

Rashid left without attending the last two sessions.

Bryony

I encountered Bryony's worry during the final lunch. She was concerned that the conference had been too structured. She felt that she had been too directed during the weekend and this detracted from her ability to get the maximum benefit from it. Being directed, she felt, prevented her from being able to be 'creative'. She felt that being aware of the potential power of anecdotes was sufficient and that too much formalising of the process (through the discussion structure used at the conference) would not serve to raise the quality of the discussion nor, necessarily, improve the quality of teaching and learning.

Bryony said she would go away and give it more thought before coming to a final conclusion.

Clare

Clare's worries emerged on the evaluation sheet. She wrote particularly of a specific session in which she felt that the task to which the introductory talk had guided participants was not what the group discussion subsequently centred on. The input in this session had been looking at issues connected with the National Curriculum and had been very specific. She also suggested that the use of anecdotes, without proper guidance from the group leader, could degenerate into 'personalised ramblings', which served no useful purpose.

THE GROUP'S REFLECTIONS

My first feeling after Rashid's worries was that he should have stayed to the end of the conference in order to give himself the chance to get a complete picture of it because the structure and purpose were gradually revealed through the sequence of the sessions. However, on reflection I felt that his worry was valuable to us because it prompted a consideration of whether the particular structure we had chosen was suitable. It raised the following questions which it seemed important to address.

- *When planning a short weekend conference centred on professional development using the anecdoting process, should we try to make its structure explicit from the start?*

- *Should participants be aware of the structure so that they can observe its emergence from a position of knowledge?*

- *Would this obviate potential bewilderment created by ignorance of the structure?*

• *On the other hand, can awareness come from someone else telling you?*

From all three sets of worries I was aware of the potentially destructive effect of differing perceptions. Bryony had described a completely opposite reaction to Rashid – for her the conference had been *too* structured. Moreover, in contrast to Clare, she suspected that much direction by the group leader had a stultifying effect on the anecdotes that were generated. Equally disturbing was the fact that the very group session Clare had chosen to criticise was one where I, as group leader, had perceived the discussion as following particularly closely the talk introducing this part of the session.

These worries point to the truth of Rashid's contention about different perceptions and different interpretations.

Such differences in a staff must be understood and considered by anyone attempting to use this way of working to implement change in their school. Clearly, the transient nature of a weekend will not allow for the resolution of these differences but can pinpoint differing perceptions as an issue capable of resolution in the longer term atmosphere of a school's whole policy.

The issue of perception is fundamental to the anecdotal way of working. From this flows all other related activity. Variations in the way people perceive situations may be as great as the number teachers in your group, but a common point for discussion can be found.

The following interlude is intended to help group leaders to consider this issue for themselves.

Perception – from *seeing* to *interpreting*

When you watch a piece of video, or listen to an anecdote, and subsequently comment on it either to yourself or to others, where is your attention focused? Have you ever said, or heard comments like,

'SHE WAS LEADING THE PUPILS TOWARDS WHAT SHE WAS THINKING'

'THE PUPIL WAS CLEARLY BORED OUT OF HIS MIND'

'HE DIDN'T GIVE THAT GIRL A CHANCE'

All of these comments are interpretations. They are indicative of the commenter's perception of what was seen, or read, or heard.

The trouble with comments like this is that they can be dismissive in their negativity. Implied is almost, 'Oh, because that teacher was so awful, I don't need to think more deeply about this.'

What did you *actually* see or hear, or read?

Perhaps in the three cases above replies to this question might be:

'THE TEACHER SAID, "BUT WHAT IF IT WAS AN *EVEN* NUMBER?"'

'I SAW A BOY ROCKING IN HIS CHAIR.'

'I HEARD THE TEACHER SAY, "NO, THAT WON'T DO SANDRA. WHAT DO YOU THINK NICKY?"'

If we were to be very pedantic, we could say that even the above statements are interpretive. What I say that the teacher said is a result of my perception of what I heard. I can convey with my tone of voice, and possibly subtle changes in wording, something which is very different to that which the teacher would say she said. The boy 'rocking in his chair' could have been trying to see the board more clearly, or getting excited by the ideas around. I can convey my view that he was bored by how I intone the words 'rocking in his chair'. Of course there may be more evidence for boredom, like perhaps the expression of his face. In that case I ought to include this information too to support any contention which I make.

The word seeing *is often used to mean* perceiving, *or* understanding. *What we see, or read, or hear in an anecdote could most often be more correctly expressed as what we* perceive *in the anecdote. We should always try to justify this, even if it is only to ourselves.*

'WHAT IS IT THAT MAKES ME FEEL SO NEGATIVE ABOUT WHAT I SAW?'

'WHAT IS IT THAT MAKES ME FEEL SO EXCITED, OR PROVIDES SUCH CLEAR INSIGHT?'

Ask:

What was it that I *actually* saw, or read, or heard?

Addressing this question can lead to clearer self-awareness. Asked in a group it can lead to a clearer communal awareness and a useful starting point for discussion.

Some starters for group discussion

The process of sharing anecdotes to raise issues needs some stimulus in order to begin. The purpose of the stimulus is initially to provide a basis for discussion, and enable some raising of warmth within the group. We can suggest a number of possibilities which we have tried out with teachers.

1. VIDEO-ANECDOTES

A short excerpt from a classroom video recording could be used to start off a session, acting as a video-anecdote. Probably five to ten minutes is an appropriate length. If it is longer than this then it will be hard for people to remember all that they have seen as well as taking up a disproportionate amount of the session time.

It is important that participants are encouraged to relate what they see to their own experience, so an excerpt should be chosen to which the group is likely to be able to relate. The 1-2-4 process can be used as follows.

1. *Individuals asked to reconstruct for themselves what they saw in the videotape, as far as possible without interpretation.*

2. *In pairs they should try to agree on what they saw, again as far as possible without interpetation.*

3. *In groups of 4 (or up to 7), share moments of significance and try to account for their significance in terms of what was actually seen in the video.*

An advantage of using video is that it provides a vivid shared experience on which everyone is able to comment. It allows everyone the opportunity to take part, so that in this respect it is non-threatening. However, the importance of the video excerpt is to trigger anecdotes from the group, in order for issues to be raised. A danger of using video is that video excerpts can be very compelling and it is tempting to dwell in the particular example which the video provides rather than moving to think about experiences and the issues which this raises for members of the group. It is all too easy to talk in terms of the teacher in the video, even though little is known about the context of the video or the objectives of the teacher concerned. An important aspect of the group leader's role where video is concerned is to encourage participants to speak of their own experience rather than try to interpret that of the teacher viewed.

It is common for participants to be adversely critical of the teacher in the video (it seems to happen whatever video is chosen!), and this can lead to very unproductive and often unprofessional remarks. The group leader can help to avoid this by suggesting that an atmosphere of respect for the teacher viewed should prevail.

Examples of sessions based on video-recording are included in Part II, sections 1 and 3, and in section 5 below.

2. WRITTEN ANECDOTES

Three brief anecdotes from teachers, written on a sheet of A4 paper have been used as a starter for some sessions (see Part II, sections 2 and 3 for examples). Participants were first of all asked to read all three anecdotes, then individually to choose the one which seemed most potent and to reflect briefly on what aspects of the anecdote related to their own experience.

They were then asked, in pairs to share their thinking, possibly exchanging anecdotes of their own. Members in any pair might originally have chosen different anecdotes, but this should not affect the ability to share.

When groups of four (or up to 7) joined together, they were asked to share something of significance which had arisen from the individual reflection or the discussion in pairs.

Rather surprisingly, on one of the occasions described in Part II and others which we have noticed, although the three anecdotes were chosen separately and not for their common features, anecdotes and issues arose from them which linked them strongly together. This suggested that the use of written anecdotes in this way was a strong focusing device for initiating discussion and reaching for issues.

An anthology of anecdotes is provided in Part VIII from which a selection could be chosen.

3. AUDIO ANECDOTES

Rather than provide anecdotes written on paper, it is possible to provide an audio-recording of a teacher telling an anecdote. This allows intonation and emphasis to be part of the anecdote which is not possible when the anecdote is written on paper.

A way of working with an audio anecdote could be much the same as described with the written anecdotes above – a period of individual reflection on what aspects of one's own experience it calls to mind, followed by sharing in pairs. The sharing in pairs could involve a requirement to agree first on what each person heard, since it is not possible to refer to a written text to confirm what was said.

The group coming together could start by sharing significant elements of the individual thinking or the discussion in pairs.

Audio has some advantage over video in that there seems to be less compulsion to dwell with the individual teacher, imputing motivation, so that personal anecdotes emerge more readily. However, some participants have claimed that the audio medium is very distancing, and it is hard to relate to what is heard. Also, a poor quality of recording can be a negative influence on the response of participants.

An example of a session based on an audio anecdote is described in Part IV, section 3.

4. PERSONAL ANECDOTES

Another way of starting is to invite each person in a group to think of some episode from their own recent experience which they are prepared to share with others in the group. Some time is given initially for each person to recall an episode and reflect on it themselves.

It is important to realise that this can be extremely threatening, and the effect of being asked to think of an episode might result in some participants being totally unable to recall anything shareable. The group leader can be of help in indicating that the episode does not need to be something specially wonderful, and that almost any interchange with a pupil can reveal something which is worth sharing.

The pairs stage would involve pairs of participants in sharing anecdotes relating the episodes which they recalled. This can work well even if one of the pair has initially nothing to share. What often happens is that in listening to the anecdote from the other person, some instance is recalled which can then be shared. Even if this does not happen, it is possible for the pair to focus just on the one anecdote offered.

Sharing as a group necessitates the retelling of some of these anecdotes. As this can be lengthy, it is likely that not all anecdotes would be shared in any case, so that it does not matter if some participants did not actually recall an episode.

Retelling for the group can be effective if the anecdote is retold by the partner of the person with whom it originated. This emphasises how interpretive we are in listening to others, and how people can hear very different stories from our words than those we intended.

This type of starter has been remarked on as potentially the most powerful, but also the most threatening way of setting up a session. Participants have said that it was important to have taken part in other sessions first where the way of working (1-2-4) has been established and a degree of trust built up. It is very hard to share personal experiences when you are not sure of the reception which they will get. An atmosphere of respect is vital for this kind of sharing to be successful. If this respect and trust is present, the personal nature of the anecdotes shared can allow more direct access to important issues. There is not the impersonal level of the outsider's anecdote to act as a barrier as in the video, audio or written starters.

Various sessions have been described which were started in this way. See Part II, sections 3 and 4, and section 5 below.

Weekend[1] diary of a group leader

FRIDAY

4.30 p.m.

Good, got away before the traffic built up; arrived in plenty of time to check out the room we'll be working in. Still some concerns, never having run one of these sessions before. Taking part seems different to leading a group. There seem to me to be three stages to look out for:

> *Raising the warmth within the group: the opening anecdote sparking off conversation which will naturally bring the group's spontaneous anecdotes to the surface.*
>
> *Working on the anecdote.*
>
> *What action can we take?*

The idea of 'working on' the anecdote doesn't seem that clear any longer! Check my notes: we are looking for the 'sameness' in the spontaneous anecdotes that will allow us to identify the shared concerns.

5.00 p.m.

The LEA residential centre is very well organised, tea in the lounge, that's better! The seminar rooms are a good size. Help set up the equipment we'll be using with another session leader. Check out the video tapes for the first session. It's a good job we did — one of the TVs isn't properly tuned and we don't have the remote control handset.

6.00 p.m.

Team meeting: domestic details sorted out. I start off tomorrow with a group of advisers and advisory teachers! I wonder what they'll make of this as a method of running in-service.

8.00 p.m.

Working Together (Group activity). The opening activity ran well but the size of the course made it difficult to discuss personal feelings about what it means to work together. One teacher expressed a view of the opening activity as 'Just a game.' The bar discussion afterwards convinces me that it's more than 'just' anything. The informal discussion of the 'game' has got us of to a good start, the evening has a good atmosphere.

---

1 This account relates to one of the weekend conferences which we held to obtain teachers' feedback on the anecdoting process. See Appendix for a conference programme.

SATURDAY

9.00 a.m.

Preparing for the first session: still not happy about 'working' on the anecdote!
  Suppose the group don't have anything to say after the first ten minutes?
  What if they don't see the point?
  What if there are no common issues?

9.15 a.m.

Advisory group: we start off with a video of a teacher starting children on a mathematical investigation. The video produces lots of talking points. Talking in pairs gets everyone sharing what they saw on the video and relating it to their own experience. In my pair I'm pleased that my partner's anecdote sparks a related feeling that has a story of my own hanging close by. It works, and I can identify the process. Good!

  When we get together as a group, the common thread is 'waiting time' that pause we make as teachers, having asked pupils a question. Someone quotes research as showing that on average we only wait 1/15th of a second for a response. (I'm sure that fraction changes every time I hear about this research). Someone else gives us an example from a course on helping teachers to wait, thus giving children time to develop their own theories.

  Why didn't I realise the effect of sitting at these long tables? All seven have sat on one side in order to view the TV. The discussion is being directed at me, not the group. It feels like a cricket match, you bowl to me at the end, I'll hit it back to have it fielded.

  Much of the discussion has become very general — it flows naturally but it isn't related to direct experience. I was hoping for more stories about in-service work with teachers. I don't want them to think we've just come to chat with no overall purpose.

  Whoops — nearly out of time and I'm not sure that I've been explicit about this way of working. I talk about what has happened so far in this grouping, how the session 'warmed up', and the sense of respect we had for each others' anecdotes. As a for instance I ask if any one has a specific story related to our last general issue. Great — Neil comes up with one! Should have asked that earlier: it's coffee time.

10.30 a.m.

Over coffee, watching groups of twos and threes it's obvious that sharing anecdotes is normal conversation, this course is about formalising it in some way. Better go back up now and rearrange those tables to allow the group to talk to each other.

11.00 a.m.

Teachers group: Working, from written anecdotes, in pairs gets us all going very quickly. I feel that the group have bonded well, no need to 'warm up'. I suggested, to start with, that we read all three stories and then talk in pairs about the one that we identify or sympathise with most easily. I am surprised by the power of a few sentences — all sorts of related concerns rapidly develop. We have an odd number of people this time so three of us make up one of the groups.

This first anecdote was:

Bead chains

I observed a teacher, Helena, with a group of reception class pupils making bead chains. The beads were of many colours, some spherical some cubical. A boy, Danny, came shyly up to her and showed her his chain.

She praised him, saying how good it looked, and started to ask him some questions about it. Most of the questions were to do with 'how many?' — how many yellow beads, how may cubical beads, how may different colours. He answered the questions, apparently without any difficulty.

Then she said, 'How many more yellow ones are there than red ones?'

Danny looked puzzled so she repeated the question. His answer was seven, which was the number of red beads.

I was waiting for her next question. How would she help him to see the difference? She ruffled his hair, said that he had done well and asked if he would like to take part in another activity.

Our small group first critically reviewed the teacher's questions. What would we have done in her position? The conversation then moved onto how one of our group has become very aware of the types of questions she now asks in the classroom. Generally she avoids direct questioning that invites right (or wrong) answers. Bringing the whole group together I ask if someone would mind starting us off with a story from their own reflecting. (I sense they are fed up with the word 'anecdote'.) Angela starts us off with her problem of class questioning:

'I have very nice pupil, Lucy, who I know will not understand when I'm talking to the class. I often find myself having to say "Don't worry about it for the moment."!!'

From here the discussion focusses on 'Why do we ask questions and why do the children ask questions?' Half an hour later the main focus has switched to 'School Liaison'. It is only on reflecting on my notes as I write this up that I can pick out the issues of 'Classroom Questions' and 'School Liaison'.

The quality of discussion was very high but I feel, again, that I should have been able to mirror the issues more effectively, allowing us to talk about future action! Never mind — we meet again. I need to work on recognising issues that arise in order to steer us towards tackling them.

All the group seem very secure contributors, even Bob, whose classroom style seems to be most at odds with other colleagues. He has quickly developed confidence in this group to talk about the way he works, and he listens to others. He says over lunch how surprised he is that the short written anecdotes proved so much more effective for him than the video that contained a 'real' classroom. He did add, however, that he felt very secure with the video less so with the written starter — interesting!! (What will he think of the next session when we start from nothing?)

4.00 p.m.

Advisory Group:
I started off with:

>*'For this session can you think of something, from your own teaching experience, that is of personal significance. It might be an incident that you felt particularly pleased about. Or something that made you think 'I won't do that again.'*

I noticed a look of panic on Monica's face so assured everyone that it didn't matter if their mind was now totally blank. We shared in pairs having first asked each person to be prepared to relate their partner's anecdote to the whole group. (It might have been better not to have done it this way, Peter told us afterwards that he was so concerned about remembering his partner's story it distracted him from the discussion. Some heads nodded agreement.

I had intended that we should hear everyone's contribution straightaway but the first story kept us going for the next hour and a quarter. At the end of the session we each relayed the other possible starters. Monica found that her story arrived in her mind while listening to her partner.

Over tea I feel that Bob hasn't yet got the point. Once or twice I heard him saying 'I'm sure that we could generate hundreds of anecdotes like this if that's what they're after.'

No that's not what we are after!

Still perhaps the formal explanation of the process chart in session 4 will help.

8.00 p.m.

Teacher Group:

This session started with a general review of the process we have been involved with throughout the day. The chart certainly has helped Vanda and Alison see the activity more clearly.

In our discussion group we reviewed the day:

STARTER

Although they were very tired their enthusiasm for this way of working has grown! Janet opened with her view that the video starter was the easiest way of getting 'into' discussion. Bob repeated his surprise that the group got more out of the written anecdote than the video. (Lots of nods.) There was general agreement that starting with a story from your own experience was the most difficult.

'What was I going to say that anyone else would find interesting?'

USEFUL?

Nods of approval but some nervousness was expressed about using this method with colleagues that you know well. The discussion then centred on how much more comfortable, less threatened, secondary members felt when sharing views in mixed primary/secondary groups. They put this down to being with people they didn't know. (I wonder . . . primary groups did not offer the same explanation.) Bill then outlined how, for him, he could see this method as a very personal way of working with his four staff. As Headteacher he feels more aware of being able to respond in future to the staff meeting anecdotes. He feels that in time he can point out to them the process of working on anecdote.

QUALITY OF DISCUSSION

Surprise, surprise they all agreed that the most useful session was when they used their own anecdotes as the starter. They highlighted, in different ways, the misgivings they felt at the beginning of session 3.

STRUCTURE

I pushed them hard on this point; I have not varied the approach significantly over the three sessions.

> 'How do you feel on In Service courses when the session leader asks you to work in groups of two or three?'

They again unanimously agreed that they wanted to talk in twos first. 'Because you get a greater feeling of confidence. You feel listened to. You then take this confidence to the larger group.'

They did not, however, like describing their partner's anecdote to the whole group:

> 'I was terrified I'd miss something out so I concentrated very hard on what they were saying but I missed the point of the story.'

> 'It felt different with someone-else telling it — there was no humour.'

Well it's worked! My groups could naturally take part in the method but can now see the process more clearly.

Perceptions of Participants

'I am amazed how much we've got out of just one little story when we worked this way ... it could so easily have been a glory-story session like the ones so often held in staff rooms, but, by being diciplined, we can now talk about specific things we can do to improve the situation in class ... attainable targets not just wide generalities.'

'It does require a lot of trust though and the ability to to tell a story in such a way that others will really listen.'

'You'd expect the story-sharing to widen the discussion, but it didn't. In fact it focussed it! We could see a sameness in the stories and that's how we worked out where we could start!'

'I think we needed other people's anecdotes like the video and written stories to begin with ... that way we test out how our comments would be recieved in the group. When they were seriously taken we developed the trust and confidence to come out with our own stories about events in our own classrooms. This really needed a basis of trust because we were baring our professional souls. A positive reception really opened the way to make real progress on our teaching.'

'We regularly reflect on our teaching and so feel quite a long way down this road, but not all teachers work this way ... how do we start with all our colleagues?'

'Well I've got one hour a week when I can go and work alongside colleagues in their classrooms. I could build the basis of trust between myself and one teacher who'll have me in. We can share anecdotes about what we did over coffee and perhaps others will begin to realise that these shared experiences are not so threatening after all. Then perhaps, slowly, we'll all be able to get into this process of identifying issues to work on.'

'Mine's only a small school – formal meetings don't really seem necessary to get things going. I think it'd be much better to just swap anecdotes informally in the corridors, over coffee, wherever!'

'I think people like Heads of Departments and Maths co-ordinators kind of have the position to approach colleagues about working together this way. They could begin with those that definitely want to and the others will be drawn in eventually when they see how we all seem to gain from it.'

'It takes time to build up confidence and trust.'

THE *ANECDOTING* PROCESS

Part IV abstracts and makes explicit the process of

anecdotes → issues → action

which forms the basis of the way of working exemplified in Part II. It also considers in further detail what is meant by 'issues' and 'action'.

Contents

Introduction

Part IV offers a *process for group working* involving *anecdotes* leading to *raising issues* leading to *classroom action*.

Parts I, II and III have introduced and described a way of working for a group of teachers which involves the sharing of anecdotes in order to allow issues to be raised. The purpose of working in this way is that ultimately the raising of issues will enable a teacher to develop their way of working with pupils in the classroom. This may involve change to, or modification of classroom practice. The teacher group, continuing to work together can support a teacher in such classroom change.

In section 1, the way of working is abstracted as the *anecdoting process* – 'From anecdotes to professional development' – its various stages are identified and labelled, and links are made between the different stages.

In section 2, the question, 'What is meant by an issue?', is then raised and some examples are given.

Section 3 – 'Raising some issues' – consists of an account of a session from a recent conference in which a group of teachers respond to an anecdote recorded on audio tape, and some issues are raised.

Part IV concludes, in section 4 with some thoughts on 'What action might be possible?'

From anecdotes to professional development

ABSTRACTING THE PROCESS

The transparencies included with this pack outline the various stages of the process, and fit together, one on top of another, to build a representation of the process as a whole. If you extract the pages and lay them onto a piece of white paper, one at a time, as you read through the stages which follow, you will see the process gradually emerge. The transparencies can also be used on an OHP.

STAGE 1 – SHARING ANECDOTES

A group of teachers sit down to work together and begin with some starting activity designed to generate discussion and trigger anecdotes from their own experience (suggestions for possible ways of starting are included in Part III, section 4).

Something which one teacher hears or sees triggers an association, or *resonates* with some aspect of their own experience, and they share this with others in the group (examples of this were described in Part II).

One anecdote leads to another as teachers respond with instances from their own experience.

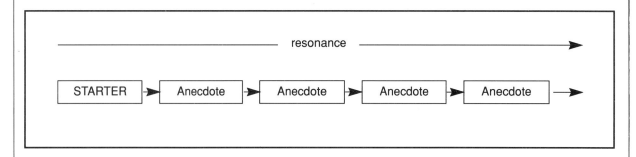

STAGE II – RAISING ISSUES

The anecdotes, having been triggered from a common starting point, and in response to other anecdotes from teachers in the group, usually have some underlying samenesses which it is possible to identify. Asking the question, 'What do these anecdotes have in common?', can lead to identification of the samenesses and to a developing sense of what issues are involved. Seeking for these samenesses in order to identify issues can be thought of as a process of *distillation* – *distilling* the issues from the anecdotes. It is likely that further anecdotes might emerge at this stage, and contribute to the identification of issues.

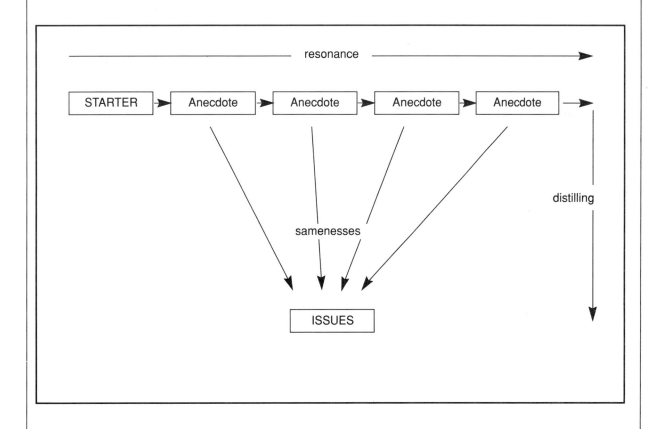

STAGE III – WORKING ON THE ISSUES

The issues which start to emerge at Stage II are likely to be fuzzy, unclear, and difficult to articulate. In order to be able to take account of such issues in the classroom, it is necessary for the group to discuss what they understand by the issues and come to some agreement about what the issues are. This may lead to further anecdotes being told by the teachers in reaching for shared meaning and understanding (some examples of issues will be offered later).

Ultimately it should be possible to articulate concisely what the issue is. At this stage the issue will have been refined to some general expression which is meaningful for the teacher group.

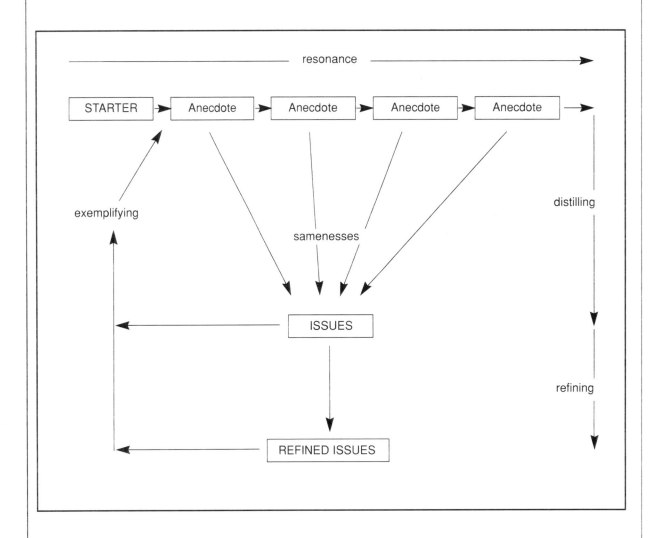

STAGE IV – CLASSROOM ACTION

This stage involves taking an issue which has been identified at Stage II and refined at Stage III and relating it to specific activity in the classroom. Each teacher would need to ask the question, 'What do I want to do as a result of recognising that this is an issue for me?'

It might involve looking out for occasions when certain things happen in the classroom, keeping a record of the circumstances and learning from what is observed. It might involve taking particular action – for example, trying out a new approach, or making some small change in behaviour.

Observations from such action could be fed back to the teacher group as anecdotes, thus stimulating continued thinking and development.

STAGE V – FEEDBACK

The process is cyclic. One of the most important aspects of it is feedback. Modifying classroom action is extremely difficult to achieve alone, and change is a lengthy process. It is ongoing group support which can make ultimate change possible. Some features of group working were described in Part III.

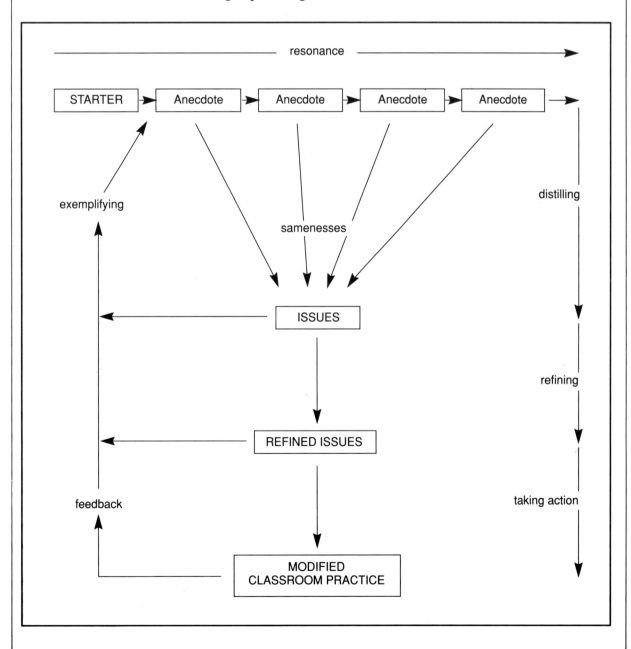

What is meant by an issue?

The word *issue* is easily used but is much less easy to define. For example some people might say that 'assessment' or 'cross-curricular-work' or 'mathematical discussion' was an issue, whereas others would prefer to say that there are many issues *related to* assessment, or to cross-curricular-work or to mathematical discussion. What may be of more value than defining the word *issue*, is to help any users of the word to get a sense of what *they* mean by it. For example, if you are particularly concerned about assessment, and perhaps have discussed aspects of it at length with a colleague, then just the word 'assessment' may be enough to recall much of your discussion and to recall for you your own issues of concern. On the other hand if you are speaking of your concerns to some stranger it might be more appropriate to go into some detail of the aspects of assessment which particularly concern you. For example, 'I get particularly worried about assessing pupils' investigative work by just considering their written report. It seems important to take into account all the thinking which I know has gone on, but which the written account does not do justice to.'

In the process outlined above, the word 'issue' is used in a very particular way to mean the concerns which underlie the anecdotes which are shared. When you tell an anecdote your very telling of it indicates some significance, and usually this remains implicit. It is not very overtly identified. However, when someone responds to your anecdote, perhaps with an expression such as, 'Yes. I have been in that situation too!', or 'Yes, I know exactly what you mean!', they are recognising some underlying significance in what you have said and responding to it. It is important to realise that *their* significance may actually be different to *yours* in telling the anecdote, so it is important not to jump to conclusions too early about 'being on the same wavelength'!

When a number of anecdotes are told, and it is possible to trace an underlying theme – the *subject* of the anecdotes, it becomes possible to extract that theme and discuss it in its own right. This is the first stage of *discipline* in the anecdoting process. If this is not tackled, the anecdotes remain no more than stories, and while they might possibly have long term impact it is more likely that they will soon be forgotten. At first the theme will be very fuzzy, and its extraction will be difficult. It needs perseverance and commitment to purpose to bring the theme, or issue, to a stage of articulation where a form of words can be produced to describe it.

The group leader role involves helping a group to persevere until such a form of words emerges. It also involves supporting the group in being able to utter ill-formed ideas without feeling foolish, because this is a vital stage. Once even one very ill-formed idea has been expressed then work can begin in refining it. Someone will say, 'No, that's not quite what I thought it was . . .', and then will hopefully struggle to give an alternative articulation. Once this begins, others will join in and the session can become productive and mutually rewarding.

A position to aim for is a form of words, however roughly composed, with which everyone can agree. It is worth writing them down, without refinement, where everyone can see them, scrutinise them and deliberate on them. It is likely then that alternative, more refined forms will be offered, because teachers hate to see ill-formed phrases written down! If not, then the group leader might suggest that some further work on refining is done. Or, it may be decided that what is there is adequate, and no further refining need be done.

The question might be asked, 'adequate for what?' and it is a crucial question. Unless there is more purpose to the process than just the intellectual identification and refining of an issue, then it might be seen as a rather sterile exercise. The purpose of identifying and refining issues is to enable professional development in the form of classroom action or change. What such action might involve is discussed in more detail later.

We end this section of Part IV with a reminder of some of the issues which were articulated and written down by teacher groups in the sessions reported in Part II. In section 2 the teachers in Jane's group produced the following list of issues emerging from the anecdotes which they discussed:

● *posing a question at the right level for a child;*

● *importance of listening to what pupils say as an indication of their thinking;*

● *recognition that a teacher's knowledge or expertise can be a barrier to helping pupils;*

● *creation of opportunities for children to communicate ideas to each other;*

● *dilemma of how to cope with ideas which pupils raise which might be conceptually too difficult for them to cope with at this stage.*

For further examples of issues arising from teacher discussion you may like to look back to Part II, Section 3 where we described the session beginning with the video excerpt on 'Ball rolling'.

It is important to realise that the forms of words which you read above are ones which the teachers involved refined from their own discussion. It is likely that they do not bear great significance for you who were not part of this discussion. When you raise, identify and refine your own issues, such words will be the result of considerable struggle and thus will bear a wealth of meaning for you.

The next section provides a further example of teachers sharing anecdotes and raising issues.

Raising some issues

■ *In this section I shall describe a one and a half hour session, held at one of the conferences, described in the Appendix, in which four teachers together with one of our team as group leader listened first to an anecdote recorded on audio-tape, and subsequently worked on it to raise issues. I shall discuss this at three levels.*

1. *Describe the session and quote from the discussion which took place.*

2. *Make remarks about the style of the session and about anecdotes and issues which were raised.*

3. *Comment on the role of group leader and on my perspective as a participant–observer of the group.*

THE RECORDED ANECDOTE

One of our purposes at the conference was to try out different starting points for discussion, and in this session it was the *audio-anecdote*. This involved an audio-recording of a teacher describing an incident which had taken place in her classroom. Due to the context of the anecdote, it was subsequently referred to as the 'Pythagoras' anecdote. The session began with the group leader Hilary, inviting the participants of the group to listen to the anecdote, which is transcribed below.

The 'Pythagoras' anecdote

> Some pupils had worked for one lesson on an investigation which was leading towards Pythagoras. One boy had been away for the first lesson and had joined them for the second lesson where they were continuing with the investigation.
>
> They'd been invited to investigate the sides of right angled triangles to see if there was any relationship between them — and this lad, the one who'd been away the previous lesson, came along and said, 'Oh, it's <u>Pythagoras</u> isn't it!' The word Pythagoras had never been mentioned, so the other people in the group said, 'What's <u>Pythagoras</u>?' So he proceeded to tell them. And then they looked back at their data and discovered that what he was saying did in fact fit their data.
>
> I asked them afterwards, 'How did you feel — when you'd been working on it for a whole lesson and this boy comes in and suddenly says — 'it's so-and-so', and it <u>is</u>?'
>
> And they didn't seem to object to that — they seemed to think that it was a legitimate thing for him to have done, and they didn't mind him telling them because suddenly they could see that it fitted their data, and in some ways it was just as fresh for them coming that way as it might have been otherwise.

The recording had not been particularly good, but although some parts had been difficult to hear, the people in the group had a fair sense of what had been described. Hilary asked them first to spend a minute or two in silence reconstructing for themselves what they had heard, and then to talk in pairs, trying to agree on what the anecdote had been about.

THE DISCUSSION

After about five minutes of pairs discussion, Hilary, who had been listening in to both pairs, suggested that this might be an appropriate point to start to share perceptions, and the group came together for further discussion.

I noticed a hiatus, albeit quite brief in this case, as participants moved from one phase of their discussion to another. I recognise that when I am group leader, I find the transition a difficult time for me – wanting it to happen, but yet wanting to be as unobtrusive as possible in making it happen. It always involves interrupting someone's thoughts or words and this seems an intrusion that is unfortunately impossible to avoid. I nevertheless feel that the three stages of 1-2-4 (see a fuller description and rationale for this in Part III) are important building blocks in creating valuable discussion, so that it is worth a small amount of disruption to communication and thinking.

Discussion began by one of the teachers commenting that she and her partner had been able to recall similar situations of their own. One teacher said,

> 'Actually, it's made me feel slightly guilty – because I think, if I'd been a teacher in that situation, I might have reacted quite badly to that child, coming back and spilling the beans – maybe I shouldn't do, but the more I think about it the more I feel I would have done.'

Another replied,

> 'If I'd been one of the girls in the group I think that I'd have been quite annoyed really . . .'

A subsequent comment was,

> 'We were saying, if I think to myself, I would have been annoyed, you automatically think – well I'm sure the kids would be annoyed – the teacher assumed they would be, and she was surprised when they weren't.' (Sic)

And then,

> 'In my classroom it happens quite a lot in a way – I have four year groups in the same class, and if I'm talking to someone saying, you know, "what do you think that is?", and other kids will come up behind and say "that's . . ." and they'll tell the kid the answer! And I get really annoyed – "GO AWAY! – we're doing this together." It happens quite a lot and I do get annoyed, and yet the child is quite happy really, because they've got the solution from the other child. Because of the age difference some of the older ones can see the younger ones doing something which they know all about.'

REFLECTION

The words which I have selected above are transcribed from the conversation, but I have not included everything which each person said due to the time it takes to transcribe and the ultimate length of this description. There are aspects of this way of working and the discussion which it makes possible which I want to emphasise.

1. *The teachers were relating the audio-anecdote to their own experience. It triggered for them associations which they recalled vividly and by sharing their own personal images they were able to come closer in understanding each other's perceptions of the Pythagoras anecdote.*

2. *The anecdote was from a secondary classroom. Two of the teachers in this discussion were in fact primary teachers, as evidenced by the last quotation above. Many issues transcend phase boundaries, and this is just an example of one such issue. Working on an anecdote in this way can lead to better cross-phase understanding and break down some of the strong but artificial boundaries which exist.*

3. *One advantage of using an audio- rather than a video-starter (see Part III, section 4) is that, rather than dwelling in the audio-anecdote, the teachers concerned turned discussion very quickly to their own experience. Video can be very much more seductive and it is therefore much harder to break away from what is seen in the video in order to reflect on one's own experience.*

In terms of anecdotes and issues orginating from the group of teachers, I have reported on one anecdote, from one of the primary teachers, and emphasised one issue which seems to be emerging in the words which I have selected. I see that issue in terms of a teacher's angry response when a pupil goes against the teacher's desired approach in the classroom. All four teachers, primary and secondary recognised such feeling of anger or annoyance when similar incidents occurred in their own classrooms. The issue at this stage was implicit in their words. There is value in making the issue overt, and I shall return to this idea later.

CONTINUING THE DISCUSSION:

One teacher asked the question,

> 'Is it right that a child can tell another child, but not the teacher (tell the child)? The children might see it better – it might be better for the children, coming from another child.'

Another commented,

> 'But it [the child telling them] would have some effect, surely, on their investigation . . . – because that's whussh, finished, isn't it?'

And then,

> 'But they did say, on the tape, that the girls did actually go back, once he'd explained it to them. They went back and found out how it fitted their data. So they did get something out of it.'

> 'They applied his theory to their data . . . yes.'

And later,

> 'The teacher on there seemed to think that they (the pupils) would be put out. She said, "How did you feel about it?", and she was quite surprised that they weren't put out. They just treated it, as you say, like information from anywhere really.'

And,

> 'But you do assume sometimes that the children are going to feel the same way as you about lots of things, and it's difficult to think to yourself sometimes, "they probably don't feel anything like I do".'

The discussion continued to consider the difference between a child giving an answer to the group and a teacher giving an answer; whether the status of the answer might be perceived differently by the group. It was pointed out that the group had checked the boy's statement against their own data, where they might not have felt it necessary to do this if the teacher had offered it to them.

Someone said,

> 'It points to how careful you need to be as a teacher, that your very authority is going to be closely involved because they're not going to challenge you, whereas they would challenge their own peers.'

One teacher reiterated that she would have been likely to have *'exploded'* in such a situation but would perhaps have regretted this later. Hilary entered the conversation at this point.

> 'It certainly threw up feelings that we knew what that felt like (many yes's here) – but I think it's also brought up the fact that children may very well react differently from the teacher telling them than they do from other children telling them. And it could be to do with, as you said, the teacher's authority, and, you know, it stops things, because the teacher's pronounced.
>
> So what is the issue here do you think. . . . ?'

Responses to this included,

> 'Don't assume that you know what the children's reactions will be – as you said, you know, we so often assume that their reactions will be our reactions and it's a very arrogant assumption.'
>
> 'One has to be adaptable, considering which direction something suddenly takes . . . to deal with the unexpected, and not to close things up.'
>
> 'And to realise the effect of an action of yours that could close things up – perhaps standing back.'

Hilary continued,

> 'And also the other thing which occurred to me was, coming back to saying that about the children, that they went back and reviewed what they'd done as a result of what was said, this is a part of investigatory work isn't it. So the catalyst provided an opportunity for reviewing. So it is a part of 243 isn't it?'

REFLECTION

243 **Mathematics teaching at all levels should include opportunities for**
- exposition by the teacher;
- discussion between teacher and pupils and between pupils themselves;
- appropriate practical work;
- consolidation and practice of fundamental skills and routines;
- problem solving, including the application of mathematics to everyday situations;
- investigational work.

Hilary's last comment may seem cryptic here, but a consideration of the elements of Cockcroft 243 and their manifestation in the classroom had been part of the overt agenda for the conference, and here Hilary was linking aspects of the conversation to this theme. I should like to address the role of group leader here briefly. Hilary had, very quietly set up the various stages of this group's activity in this session, but had otherwise mostly remained silent, simply following the conversation. This had flowed freely, and there had been no necessity for Hilary to exercise her group leader's role in respect of keeping the conversation going with appropriate interjections. However, I saw her intervention at this stage having a number of important purposes. Firstly, she summarised some of the discussion, thus making its substance potentially more overt and helping people recall some of its aspects. She then asked what the issues had been. This helped participants to reflect on the conversation and put into some concise form the underlying concerns on which discussion had been based. It had the effect of bringing out the issues more forcefully and making them available for scrutiny outside the particular trappings in which they were manifest. Thirdly she drew attention to how aspects of their conversation related to a theme on which the conference as a whole had set out to work. There are many aspects of the role of group leader, but these levels of aiding focus and synthesis seem to be particularly important. Of course it needs to be realised that the focus of the group leader will not necessarily be the same as that of all participants and so the skilful leader will help other participants to share in this focusing, possibly, ultimately, enabling the group itself to adopt the focusing role.

OVERVIEW

I see in this session a microcosm of the process which is formally described in section 1, 'From anecdotes to professional development'. From a given starting point, a group of teachers reached for issues of common concern in their experience, exemplifying their thoughts and ideas by personal anecdotes which revealed aspects of their thinking which others could share. I was very conscious that time restrictions on this session could not allow the full process to be carried through, that the stages of relating to the classroom leading to action in the classroom could not be a consideration for this group as they had no means of following it up.

Yet these stages of the process are also very personal stages. It is interesting to consider how personal aspects of the process interface with the group aspects, and how the group can enhance and support the activity and development of the individual. For example, one teacher in the group kept coming back to her reaction to the audio-anecdote, which was that she might have *exploded* in such a situation, but then regretted her reaction afterwards. She had such vehemence when she said the word 'exploded' that it was possible for the rest of us to picture her situation, and the subsequent regret which she felt. It is possible however, in being able to articulate this likely scenario for the group, and having shared discussion in and around the issue of concern, that the next time she is in such a situation in the classroom, she might be alert and aware enough to stop *just before exploding*. If so, she would then have an instant of choice, in which she could decide whether actually to explode, or whether to try out some other form of action. Whatever her choice, it would then be conscious and considered, rather than instinct or gut feeling.

The raising of the intuitive to the conscious is one way of looking at professional development. As professionals, once we are aware of aspects of our actions, we then have opportunity to change these actions, or perhaps to reinforce our belief that they are good in the circumstances. The sharing of anecdotes in and of itself is probably not sufficient to ensure this raising of consciousness, although it may have a *sub*conscious effect on activity. When we take the step to identify the issues which we have raised, as Hilary did in the session described, we start the process of bringing aspects of our practice to a conscious level, so that they are available for us to work on more directly. Much has been written of *the teacher as researcher* (see for example the ATM reference in Part VIII), and the act of being aware in the classroom of aspects of practice which we particularly wish to observe, and making those observations, is part of this researching process.

The existence of the teacher group with which to work is crucial. In the conference session described, it was not possible for the group to continue to meet after the conference. Ideally however, the group would be formed from teachers who could and would meet together at regular intervals to share aspects of their classroom work. It would then be possible to report back on incidents related to previous discussion and issues raised. It would also be possible to bring new situations and seek help and support from the group in working on them.

POSTSCRIPT

One final reflection. In the anecdote, the group to whom the boy came back and told about the Pythagorean relationship consisted all of boys. It is interesting that the above teachers talk about the 'girls' in the group?

What *action* might be possible

The purpose of identifying and refining issues is to enable professional development in the form of classroom action or change.

These words are from section 2, 'What is meant by an issue?' However, they form the crux of this entire pack which offers a way of working which can lead to significant professional development.

For any teacher, significant professional development need not mean dramatic change in the classroom, but it must mean the development of a greater *awareness* of what is done in the classroom and the reason *why* it is done. This increased awareness is likely to lead to change, albeit not necessarily involving major or immediate alteration to classroom practice.

For example, relating to what was written in 'Raising some issues' in section 3, if you were one of the teachers concerned, possible action resulting from the session described could involve:

1. *To be on the lookout for instances of pupils giving answers to other pupils.*

2. *To keep a notebook somewhere in the classroom and jot down very briefly something about these instances as you notice them, as a reminder to yourself.*

3. *To reflect, when time allows, on what you did, how you felt about it, and what you wish you had done.*

4. *To decide whether some alternative approach might be appropriate in dealing with such instances if they happen again.*

5. *To try out the alternative approach and reflect on the outcome as in (3).*

6. *To share the results of any of the above with the teacher group.*

Number 1 of these relates directly to the particular issues with which these teachers were concerned, and this would necessarily vary from one group of teachers to another. However, the other five points are general ones which could apply to any situation. The anecdote which follows comes from one member of the writing team, and relates to an instance of number 2 above.

Example of classroom action arising from a group session

I was working with a group of teachers on a professional development course, trying to get at issues which were of concern to them in their teaching. I had asked them each to think of a personal anecdote which they could share as a starter for discussion. When discussion was well under way and issues were emerging, one teacher wryly commented that the most difficult part of this way of reaching for issues was, for her, thinking initially of an anecdote to share. She said, 'I know that lots of significant moments occur when I am in the classroom, but I can never think of them afterwards. I suppose I ought to write them down, but somehow there is never time.'

This clearly accorded with the experience of others in the group, because they were nods and murmurings of assent. The course they were studying required them to report on incidents from their classroom which were of significance, so it was actually important to find some way of remembering them. They seemed to see 'writing down' as writing a detailed or lengthy account.

I asked what they might do that would help and as a result of further discussion it was suggested that just jotting down the odd word or two when an incident occurred might be sufficient to help recall the incident later.

At the next meeting of the group, one of the teachers quite suddenly said, 'Oh, by the way, I did what we suggested last time. I kept a piece of paper on my desk, and, whenever something occurred which I wanted to remember, I instantly — or as soon as I could — went over to my desk and jotted down a few words. It actually worked. I could, then think back afterwards and recall what happened.'

In response to this, another of the teachers said that she had done the same, and that it had worked for her too. It seemed to me, reflecting on this, that here was a very good example of classroom action which arose from working on anecdotes and raising issues. It was not a big deal. It was in fact quite a small task to undertake. Yet for two teachers it was effective because they were successful in what they set out to achieve.

In their case they needed to remember incidents in order to report on their classroom work for course assessment. However, one aspect of developing as a teacher involves recalling incidents from the classroom, reflecting on them and possibly basing future work on the result of this reflection. The piece of paper, or possibly a small notebook, could be an invaluable aid to reflection. Just by being there, available, it encourages the jottings for reminders.

It was significant for me because it seemed in some sense the right 'size' of task to undertake. The idea of taking action in the classroom as a result of raising issues can seem formidable, because I think, people see 'action' as needing to be big and important and ambitious. In fact, setting yourself quite a small task, relatively speaking, can be much more effective, and therefore rewarding, satisfying and confidence building, because it has much more chance of success.

An example of number 4 above was reported in Part II, section 3, where Sajid, Joanna's teacher set a target for his future work in his classroom. This involved trying out a slightly different way of approaching the problem which he saw with Joanna. He said,

'Joanna, . . . very able, but attracts such adverse attention because she's always pointing out the mistakes of her classmates – a clever clogs of the worst kind! Till now, Joanna has been causing relationships to go rapidly from bad to worse.

'That discussion about building up a history of success inspires me to have a chat with Joanna suggesting that, instead of putting her peers down, she could actively look for something that is said or done that is right, and make that a basis for discussion. I will watch out for evidence of this new positive behaviour, and praise both Joanna for using it, and the other pupils for entering into a dialogue with Joanna to build a clearer understanding. This could build histories of success all round. You know, I can see a real chance of changing the whole atmosphere of my class by doing this.'

If Sajid had actually taken the action which he proposed, he would then have been in a position to reflect on its outcome as suggested in number 5, and possibly to discuss this outcome with the teacher group as suggested in point number 6. It is likely that the action taken might not have resulted in exactly the outcome which the teacher hoped for, and subsequent discussion with the group could enable the teacher to presevere with the action, or to modify it as appropriate. Taking such action alone can be a daunting and lonely business. If it does not work as envisaged, it is all too easy to count it as a failure and do nothing further, except perhaps be less ready to envisage such action on other occasions. The teacher group can provide support for further reflection and action, suggesting reasons for why certain things occurred, and providing helpful suggestions for what might be done next. In Part V, the case studies relating to teachers working on the National Curriculum provide further examples of the process of

anecdotes → issues → action.

Points 2 to 6 above encompass three majr principles which could form the basis of successful classroom action following the raising of issues:

- *looking out for examples*, or manifestations in the classroom of some issue which has been identified OR *instigating some action* in the classroom as a result of some issue which has been identified;

- *reflecting on* what is observed, or what occurs in the classroom;

- *sharing* this reflection *with the teacher group* for support and encouragement to enable further action.

The result of applying these principles may not lead to dramatic change, but experience shows that it will lead to greater awareness and to the increased ability of a teacher to reflect critically on everyday practice thus enabling potential improvement.

APPLYING THE ANECDOTING PROCESS

Part V concerns the holding of professional development sessions which are focused on a given theme – for example, the National Curriculum, TVEI, Primary–Secondary Liaison, or Teaching Styles.

It begins by offering advice in setting up sessions in which the anecdoting process might be used, and continues with three case studies of particular sessions. The focus of these sessions was particular attainment targets of the National Curriculum in mathematics.

Contents

Introduction

This section moves from consideration of the anecdoting process in general terms to particular ways of implementing it in professional development sessions.

Part IV described the process, starting with anecdotes and leading to the identification of important underlying issues in the teaching and learning of mathematics. This might then precipitate action in the classroom related to specific aspects of a teacher's classroom practice on which the teacher might decide to work.

Part V shows how potent that process can be when applied to teachers' specific concerns.

If you have participated in sessions with other teachers where you have focused on some area of concern such as those given on the next page, stop for a moment to reflect on the way in which the sessions were started. What were their typical features?

Try to identify what you felt was successful or unsuccessful about the sessions and consider your reasons for this.

Part V considers an approach to such sessions using the process of starting with anecdotes to raise issues, refining these issues, and working towards classroom action.

Professional development sessions

(i) The form and focus of a session

 Suppose that you wish to set up, run, or participate in a session in which a group of teachers work on a declared focus.

For example:

- **The National Curriculum –**
  - *developing a programme of study;*
  - *how to work with pupils on a given attainment target;*
  - *what activities might support a particular target level?*

- **TVEI**
  - *how can we link with other subjects to the advantage of pupils?*
  - *how can the whole curriculum be related to the 'world of work'?*

- **Primary–secondary liaison**
  - *what issues transcend the phase boundary?*
  - *how can we provide continuity for pupils?*

- **Teaching styles**
  - *how do we interpret Cockcroft 243?*
  - *what does mathematical discussion involve?*
  - *when is exposition appropriate and when not?*

- **Departmental concerns**
  - *what homework policy can be most effective?*
  - *what are the issues in GCSE assessment?*
  - *using pupil errors positively.*

- **Whole school concerns**
  - *teaching a subject/topic with which you feel insecure;*
  - *how we organise our classrooms;*
  - *what professional development means for us.*

It is likely that sessions in which you have taken part have involved one or both of two features:

1. *A plenary address from some 'expert'.*

2. *Groups of teachers with a large sheet of paper and a felt-tip marker.*

It is common to hear phrases like, 'I just get bored listening to someone else and my attention wanders', or 'If someone again sends me into a group with a large sheet of paper and a felt tip pen I shall scream!'

Possibly if you identify the activities you feel are not successful for you in these sessions, the reasons may include that they are used inappropriately or too frequently. An unremitting dose of any one pattern is likely to produce feelings of resentment. It is possible to imagine someone saying, 'If I hear the word *anecdote* again I shall scream!'

What this pack offers is not a panacea to cope with all occasions, so that teachers will never again have negative feelings, but an alternative which we believe to have value. Its value lies in its encouraging teachers to get to the root of their concerns, to identify not necessarily the global issues, but the issues which are closest to home and about which some action might have a chance of success.

WHAT IS THE FOCUS OF A SESSION? WHO DECIDES?

Fundamental to the success of the application of this process is that participants declare the focus, that this is not imposed by some external agency. This implies that time needs to be given to negotiating the focus.

However, if the group of teachers concerned is not used to working with anecdotes to raise issues, it might be best to have first a number of sessions where the anecdoting process is the focus of the sessions. A group of several such sessions is described in Part II.

The group-leader's role is crucial to the success of the anecdoting approach, particularly when a group is inexperienced in its use. Many examples of the group leader role are described in Part II, and the role is addressed more explicitly in Part III.

ADVANTAGES OF THE ANECDOTING APPROACH

It can be very difficult to tackle hard issues head on. Indeed, it might not be clear initially just what these issues are, or in particular what their implications are for the group participants.

When sessions are dominated by the more articulate, the more aggressive, the more 'knowledgeable' members of a group, this can mean that others are unable or reluctant to speak, and therefore never really enter the thinking in a valuable way or get the chance to contribute.

The anecdoting approach offers everyone the chance to get involved and encourages participation at a teacher's *own* level with the teacher's own concerns.

The discipline of looking for sameness in anecdotes, and reaching towards general issues, as described explicitly in Part IV, promotes genuine common understanding between teachers and provides a chance to be effective in a way which is most suitable to the teachers involved.

(ii) How to begin

Choose a focus which is a sincere concern for all participants.
The focus would be most likely to be chosen before the group meet together, so that preparations for the meeting can take place accordingly. The environment is important. It helps to meet in comfortable surroundings where people can sit together informally. Cups of tea or coffee at the start can help relaxation.

A major aim is to get everyone involved in the thinking at their own level.

The purpose of the anecdoting process is to encourage a flow of anecdotes from individual participants. From this, the issues which arise are likely to be of direct relevance to those concerned.

How do you stimulate personal anecdotes?

Two ways are suggested.

1. *Offer one or more prepared anecdotes in written audio or visual form (see Part III, section 4).*

2. *Invite each member of the group to offer a personal experience, view, concern etc. to share with others.*

USING A PREPARED ANECDOTE

WHAT?

When the focus of a session has been agreed, the group leader, or others who undertake the planning for the session, could look for particular prepared anecdotes which seem to speak to the declared focus.

WHERE?

Part VIII in this pack contains a bank of written anecdotes. These might contain one or more which are relevant to your focus. There may be video or audio tapes which you could use – we provide some references, also in Part VIII.

HOW?

The way of using such a prepared anecdote has been exemplified in Part II and discussed further in Part III with regard to the 1-2-4 process. Briefly, get participants to read, watch or listen, then spend a minute or two in silent reflection asking 'What did I see, or hear, or read', and relating this to their own experience. Questions like, 'What does this remind me of in my classroom; in my teaching?' or 'What questions does this raise for me?' or 'What related experiences have I had?', can be helpful in encouraging participants to come up with related anecdotes of their own. Sharing in pairs after this allows everyone a chance to speak to one other and starts getting ideas out into the open. Full group discussion can then follow as appropriate.

Once anecdotes start to be shared, the process of identifying the issues and working on these issues is as described in Part II and abstracted in Part IV. The group leader is essential in stopping conversation rambling, in encouraging the search for sameness in the anecdotes and identification of issues, and in reaching for the crucial implications of an issue for classroom work. It is then that the group can begin to suggest what action they might undertake, and individuals can get a sense of what they might actually do in the classroom.

BUT BEWARE . . .

Prepared anecdotes carry an inherent danger. If participants in the group do not relate well to the introductory anecdote, whether it is written on paper, or in the form of a piece of video, the result may be very negative, with participants' energy being spent on criticising the material – or on saying why they do not wish to engage with it. (Particular examples of this may be found in Part VII – 'An equal opportunities INSET day' and 'Working and not working.')

It must be recognised that this negativity is in the participants and not in the material, but it has resulted from the stimulus of the material. It is very hard for a group leader to know in advance how all individuals will react to a chosen anecdote.

A determined attitude to such materials can avoid some unfortunate and uncomfortable time wasting. This involves an agreement to be only positive. It must be recognised that negativity may allow vituperative energy release, but not much more, and that it is in everyone's interest to try to gain something from the experience. The most important aspect of being positive involves asking questions about one's own situation. 'What am I reminded of in my situation which causes questions or concern?' 'What could I usefully work on with the help of my colleagues?' If the focus is approached in this way, then it is likely that the starting anecdote will be no more than that, and that the energy of the session will be firmly where it is most required – in the professional concerns of the individuals taking part.

USING ANECDOTES FROM THE GROUP

This begins with an anecdote.

Something 'big' or 'important'

An Open University tutor was working with a group of teachers who had to report and reflect on some significant event or incident from their classroom for a piece of assessed work. Various teachers in the group started to raise objections to what it was they had been asked to do.

For example,
'I'm only a supply teacher. I don't get much opportunity to do extended investigations with the pupils that I meet.'

'We're concentrating so hard now on finishing the syllabus, that I can't find any really interesting session to talk about.'

The tutor suddenly got the sense that they were panicking because they were interpreting 'some significant event' as being something <u>big</u> and <u>important</u>. She therefore set them the following task.

'Think back to last week, or some recent lesson. Recall just <u>one</u> occurrence of talking with a pupil or with a group of pupils, or just <u>one</u> thing which someone said to you, or just <u>one</u> thought which you had when you were talking, or watching, or listening to pupils.'

She was then silent, and maintained the silence for about a minute, then asked,

'Has everyone managed to think of just one thing?'

There were nods all round, so she then asked,

'Would you now turn to the person next to you and share the moment which you've just thought about with each other.'

The discussion in pairs was avid, and could have gone on for considerable time. After about ten minutes, she drew the group together to share what they had discussed in pairs. There were many classroom issues arising from the situations discussed. There were also issues related to the exercise — it took only the requirement to think of <u>one small ordinary</u> episode for everyone to be absorbed in thinking about teaching and learning.

One way to start the group's thinking of their declared focus is to ask each person, silently, to think of one small episode from their classroom which relates in some way to the focus.

It could be an interaction with one pupil or a group of pupils. It could be something which occurs frequently which the teacher would like to change. It could be a thought which the teacher has when certain things happen. It could be a worry or concern. It could be a wish which somehow never seems to be fulfilled. It could be a desire to find out more about something in particular.

If there is someone who truly cannot think of anything, this does not matter, as it is likely that in talking with others, something will be triggered. The tutor in the anecdote above reported that often in such sessions, when one teacher thought he had nothing to contribute, something quickly arose from talking with others.

The sharing in pairs allows initial unease to be dispelled as each person gets used to the sound of her own voice and the reassuring similarity of the other person's thoughts and feelings.

As in most group sessions, the group leader's role here is important. Anecdoting gains momentum, and it is easy for discussion to flow wide of the focus. It is then up to the group leader to make participants aware of this so that the group can decide whether to pull back to their focus, or to go is some other direction which is proving interesting and fruitful. Whichever is decided, it is important to stop rambling, and be disciplined in getting to the nub of the issues which emerge. A satisfactory conclusion for any session is to have some ideas for classroom action which can be put into practice tomorrow.

(iii) Being aware of the anecdoting process

In the anecdote described above, the tutor was able *in the moment*, to suggest an activity appropriate to the group. This involved the use of anecdotes to raise issues and encourage action. The words *in the moment* indicate a state of mind in the group leader which is important for such an activity to be proposed and to have a chance of success.

The first requirement of the group leader is *being aware*. When you have worked in this way often, and are convinced of its potential, then it is likely to come to mind readily when a situation arises which could benefit from it. You can then find an opportunity to set it in motion.

The second requirement is to have some confidence in the process, perhaps because you *are* convinced of its potential, so that you can introduce it with confidence evident in your voice and action. This helps others to believe that what they are being asked to do is likely to be productive, and therefore to take part positively.

The message here is that you do not necessarily need to plan a session in terms of anecdoting, but simply to be aware of the anecdoting process so that if an opportunity arises, you can suggest an appropriate activity. This avoids the slightly artificial nature of some starts to sessions in which participants are not yet familiar with the process and find it difficult to perceive the reasons behind what they are being asked to do.

It is also true, that once a group becomes used to working together and familiar with the use of anecdotes to raise issues, that an anecdoting mode can be engaged without any overt move to instigate it. It becomes a quite natural part of working together.

Three case studies

This section consists of three case studies which describe how the anecdoting process may contribute to professional development work related to some agreed theme. In this case the theme is the National Curriculum, which is particularly topical at the time of writing this pack, as the National Curriculum is just being introduced into schools and most teachers are thinking about its implementation. However, any of the themes mentioned on page 84, or indeed others, could have been the subject of the teachers' concern. Our purpose in offering these case studies is to exemplify the approach used. Giving three *examples is deliberate. The* theory of sameness and generalisation, *offered in Part VI, explains the importance of offering a number of examples from which it is then possible to start to generalise. Three examples may be seen as the minimum for which this is possible.*

(i) Reporting on the National Curriculum

This case study is taken from a group session in which colleagues were discussing attainment targets and how to report on pupils' work and school schemes of work to parents and governors. It shows powerfully how an anecdote from one teacher led to an issue that showed the whole group how they could learn to report publicly about what they were doing in class and how the words used in the National Curriculum could provide a bridge between parents and governors and the teachers. Furthermore, in the face of criticism from parents and governors about the heavy use of calculators in the key stage 1 years, and the fear that this would impair the pupils' grasp of 'the basics', the teachers discovered how use of the National Curriculum Attainment Targets to report on existing practices in fact provided an excellent justification for their continued use of calculators.

David, a member of the CAN[1] project in PrIME,[2] told how one six-year-old explained her way of finding the answer to 324 taken 26 times; she said, 'Well ten lots of 324 is easy. It's 3240 so I'll take 10 lots of 324 and then another ten lots, then I'll take 5 lots which is just half of ten lots, add all that together, and then add on one more lot of 324 to give me 26 of 'em.'

David said: 'You see I don't want to be *bound* by targets like those in the National Curriculum – I want to be target free! I want to be free to go down the avenues the children are following! If I'd had to follow the levels in the National Curriculum I couldn't have allowed six-year-olds to do things like that!'

Someone in the group then said, 'Hang on David, just let's look at the National Curriculum targets on Number and Number operations – Target 2 level 1, did you do that? (David: 'Yes.') Level 2? Level 3? Level 4? (David: 'Yes most of those.') And Target 3, would you say your calculator activities had addressed levels 1, 2, 3, 4 and 5? (David: 'Yes, all of those!') 'Well, that's pretty fantastic for a six-year-old programme of study!'

What then emerged was the issue of *not* seeing the targets as building upon what can and can't be done but rather as a way of talking about the objectives one is holding for any given programme of work.

---

1 CAN stands for Calculator Aware Number.
2 PrIME stands for Primary Initiative in Mathematics Education (see Part VIII).

The group decided that instead of using talk like 'being target free', which is enough to turn grey any parent/governor/inspector brandishing the National Curriculum orders, we could report that:

> *'whilst using the calculators to investigate the combination of numbers using the four operations identified in Attainment Target 3 and exploring various methods of doing the calculations, David had in mind achievement at any or all of the first five levels. Anita's explanation of her method for calculating 324 × 26 shows knowledge, skills and understanding at level 5. This is a level expected of the top 10% of eleven-year-olds and most fourteen-year-olds. Being only six-years-old, Anita is clearly thriving under the Calculator Aware Number approaches used in David's school. What is more, since Anita's explanation was broadly typical of her classmates this level of attainment seemed to justify the investigative use of calculators at Key Stage 1.'*

Such a use of the National Curriculum to report on work done in the classroom and methods used was clearly much more powerful than David's earlier 'I want to be target free' statement. His anecdote had provided a basis for this issue to become clear for the group of teachers. They agreed that here was a way forward for work on the National Curriculum – to use the levels and targets to analyse what they were already doing and then report accordingly. It was exciting, in this instance, to finish up with a very potent argument for continuing with their calculator work rather than seeing the National Curriculum as a document that would put an end to calculators in the infant classroom. Perhaps all in the group would discover similar things about their existing practice too!

(ii) Attainment Target 5 (Number/Algebra) – Expressing Generality

This target speaks of pupils being able to recognise and use patterns, relationships, and sequences, and make generalizations. In particular level 4 refers to 'generalise, mainly in words, patterns which arise in various situations'; and level 7 refers 'use symbolic notation to express the rules of sequences'.

This case study illustrates how teachers in a mathematics department decided to spend an INSET training day on the topic of Expressing Generality, *using the Open University UPDATE pack of that name (Mason, (1989), see Part VIII). The pack suggested the teachers do three activities on their own and then discuss the outcomes with one another.*

The activities were:

Activity 1

Look at the following sequence. How would you make the next picture in the sequence?

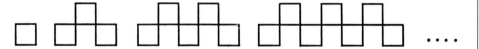

And the next?
Now express in words *how* the pictures are to be continued.

Activity 2

How many squares will be needed to make the 37th and the 100th pictures in the following sequence?

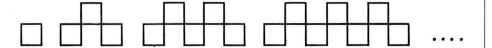

What role is being played by 37 and 100?

Activity 3

Someone is thinking of a position in the following sequence, but we don't know precisely which one. Find a way to tell them how to calculate the total number of squares needed to make their particular picture in the sequence.

The teachers worked together on these activities as suggested. They then all agreed to try them out in just one of their maths classes during the next few days.

Netta, feeling a little uncertain of just how to do this with her class of particularly disenchanted 5th year low attainers, but nevertheless wanting to have a go, arranged for the Head of Department to work in alongside.

She drew the sequence

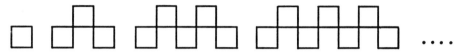

on the board, inviting the pupils to see if they could explain how to draw the next one. Mellissa, normally very antagonistic to mathematics, suddenly exclaimed: 'Oh yes, look! It's like paw prints in the sand. The dog's got three toes and the number of paw prints you need is always one less than the position!' She subsequently improved her statement when another pupil pointed out, 'That's not quite right, because one toe mark is shared in each paw print.' Discussion raged for the full 40 minutes lesson with varying generalities usually in words, coming from every pupil in the class.

Netta shared this experience as an anecdote with her colleagues during the next departmental meeting. Many of them recognised that they had experienced similar apprehension about trying the ideas out. All, however, now acknowledged the importance of giving time to expressing generality. They then had a shot at writing down what they now saw the process of *Expressing Generality* to involve. At this point Ann said, 'You know when we first did that activity on the INSET Day I thought it was trivial. Anyone could see it was $n-1$ on the top and n on the bottom! Having tried it with my second years and listened to Netta, I now see how important it really is. My lot went through every single stage of the first three activities in this pack! I think we should do more of these . . . just little one lesson slots every now and then. We should do some of these (pointing to further activities in the Resources at the back of the *Expressing Generality* – UPDATE pack).'

For these teachers it had not been evident what might be involved in 'expressing generality' for those who were inexperienced mathematically, such as their pupils. When the teachers had done the activities themselves, the generality had seemed obvious and they had been able to jump immediately to generalisations expressed in symbolic form, e.g. (n–1) squares above, and n squares below in the given pattern.

However, the symbolic expression of general patterns is not obvious or natural to pupils, and many pupils need to go through some stage of informal articulation of the patterns they see before any more formal expression can be made. Mellissa's 'paw prints' was a very good example of this, and it was Netta's sharing of this episode, as an anecdote, which brought the issue into the open for the teachers. The anecdote resonated with their own experiences with their own pupils, and the purpose of the original activities suddenly became very clear. As a result they agreed that offering pupils further examples of this type of activity would be useful in helping them to express patterns more clearly.

This example illustrates well the recurring sequence of anecdote → issue → action. *In this case, as a result of agreed classroom action, anecdotes were shared, an issue became apparent, and further action was planned. During this process the teachers' awareness of the value of encouraging pupils to express their own generalities developed and they were able to perceive new possibilities for the classroom.*

(iii) Attainment Target 10 Shape and Space

This target requires pupils to be able to recognise and use properties of 2D and 3D shapes. Level 7 requires pupils to 'understand and apply Pythagoras' Theorem' and gives us an example: 'Calculate a side of a right handed triangle when the other two sides are known.'

Continuing on from the experiences on Expressing Generality in the maths department quoted above, this case study concerns the transfer of generalising skills to syllabus topics like the one described in Attainment Target 10, level 7. This led the teachers to consider the issue of what it means to work investigatively beyond the realm of investigations and into all the syllabus content implied by the National Curriculum.

Encouraged by the successful experience of working alongside Netta, the Head of Department had made opportunities to work with other colleagues in their classrooms. He used two or three of his untimetabled periods to do so.

One such shared experience with a colleague several weeks later proved a real break through. During a lesson on solving right-angled triangles both teachers recognized a possible new perception of the process of expressing generality. The class of average ability, having done several lessons on the topic, were working through an exercise which had twenty-one similar problems, involving the use of Pythagoras' theorem. With twenty minutes left of the double period and only 10 examples completed the Head of Department asked the class to put pens down and then said: 'Looking at each of the examples you have worked through; can you see anything the same about what you did to get your answers on each occasion – anything the same?' Here was an opportunity for the pupils to express in their own words what was needed to solve right-angled triangles. Needless to say this was not a trivial task for these 4th year pupils, but many of them made an attempt. Neil's first attempt, concerning a right triangle with shorter sides of 3 and 5 units, was, 'If you take the hypotenuse and square it, that's the area. Then if you square the 3 and the 5 and add them, you find it's the same as the hypotenuse.'

The teacher asked, 'What do you think of that Melanie?' and Melanie replied, 'You square them two, and add them. Then that's the hypotenuse.'

By the end of the period almost all pupils could explain in some form, and in particular Melanie was able to amend her explanation to,

'You square the 3 because that's the area of the square on the 3 side. You do the same for the area on the 5 side and then you add them. That's the square on the long side opposite the right angle. Then you square root.'

It seemed from their generalisations that Neil and Melanie and half the class had acquired a real understanding of Pythagoras as a result of being given time specifically to pull all the past experiences with Pythagoras together and state the sameness they saw.

What impressed the whole department when this anecdote was shared in another departmental meeting was that it had taken no longer than the time planned by the teacher to spend on Pythagoras. What's more, they saw that this direct transfer of the expressing generality process to syllabus topics had the potential to help improve pupils' understanding of the mathematics.

This extended perception of the process of expressing generality generated a new desire to try out the application of expressing generality skills to whatever syllabus topic was currently in hand.

Evaluating their experiences at the end of the term one teacher commented on the long time spent on just the one idea:

'Without that amount of time, none of us could ever have seen how non-trivial the process of Expressing Generality in Attainment Target 5 is for pupils, nor how important it is to use expressing generality skills in our everyday teaching.'

Again we can trace here the cycling process of anecdote → issue → action. As a result of the work which the teacher group had done on the expression of generality and the importance of helping pupils to express the patterns which they saw in their own informal way, two teachers were in a position to notice an instance of where this could be of practical value in a lesson. In the routine exercise which the pupils were doing in order to get extra practice on the use of the Pythagorean result, the teachers saw an opportunity to work directly on the expression of generality. Each question in the exercise was just one example of the use of Pythagoras' theorem. By asking pupils to try to articulate what the questions had in common, they enabled pupils to express Pythagoras' theorem for themselves, thus making it their own. This was likely to have far more meaning for them than just the implicit understanding of the theorem through tackling a number of questions in an exercise. The realisation of the teacher group, when this episode was reported to them, that any exercise has as its purpose some implicit generality, led the group to an awareness of how they might help pupils to reach a better understanding of general mathematical results.

The issue for the teachers lay in seeing an extension to their work on expressing generality in terms of pupils' increased understanding of syllabus topics. The group work, sharing anecdotes from the classroom, led to further potential for classroom action.

SUMMARY

Each of the examples given above shows how teachers have been able to move from global concerns like 'What will be involved in National Curriculum assessment and reporting?' and 'How can we develop pupil attainment in Expressing Generality?' to very specific activities in their classrooms. These activities threw considerable light on the teachers' declared concerns enabling them to develop their own views on productive ways forward.

The section has also made suggestions about ways and means of getting a group going on the anecdoting process. At the very heart of all these suggestions is the belief that the best way to develop ideas about any aspect of our professional lives is by doing things in schools, reflecting on the outcomes and sharing the results of our activities with colleagues. We then move forward together as a result of working investigatively in this way; not trying slavishly to implement someone else's solutions to our problems, but boldly and positively developing our own responses to the concerns that face us.

This investigative view of human learning finds expression in a theory of sameness and generalisation which is what all human beings do when trying to make sense of a wide variety of experiences. The next section describes this theory and demonstrates the universality of the approach for teachers and pupils alike.

VI

A THEORY OF SAMENESS AND GENERALISATION

*Part VI abstracts a theory which
describes an investigative process
of looking for samenesses and
forming generalisations at a
number of levels. One level is the
distilling of issues from
anecdotes; another involves the
application of the anecdoting
process to effective professional
development.*

*An example is given of the
application of this theory to
concerns about cross-curricular
issues.*

Contents

Introduction

Part VI begins by describing the investigative processes which might be used in formulating any concept. It then goes on to show how such a view of learning is just as applicable in a staff room where teachers are trying to formulate ideas about professional issues confronting them.

A way of working with pupils in developing mathematical concepts can be seen as a model for a way of working cooperatively as a staff, and an internal consistency emerges between the way in which we as teachers learn, and the way in which we might teach – a kind of 'do as you would be done by' pedagogy.

We show how this way of working might be applied to particular issues of teaching related to cross-curricular initiatives.

The investigative process – abstracting the sameness from a series of special cases

1. MATHEMATICAL INVESTIGATING

Recall, for a moment, any mathematical investigation you have recently carried out either as an adult or with children. What were some of the significant activities that you and the participants engaged in?

Was there a stage where particular cases of some mathematical idea were explored one by one? Like this:

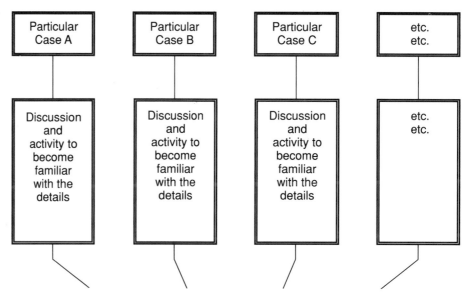

Did there come a time where those involved in the investigation became aware of an underlying sameness, or pattern, in all of the special cases – a kind of drawing together of all the experiences so far?

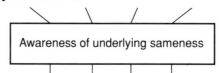

And was subsequent activity focused on further discussion to try and reach agreement in the group as to what, precisely, that underlying sameness was – a movement from seeing sameness to articulating that sameness?

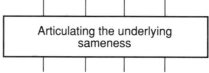

And was there finally, a move to check that what had been discovered always worked and, that furthermore, one could convince others of its merit – especially the sceptics? Perhaps that set the whole investigation off all over again as new, hitherto unthought of insights began to emerge demanding further exploration·

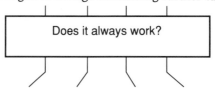

Putting all these phases of an investigation together we come up with a model of the investigative process employed by learners as they formulate their own view of concepts. The diagram below has been annotated to describe the activity of the learners and various stages in the learning process.

A model of the investigative process of learning

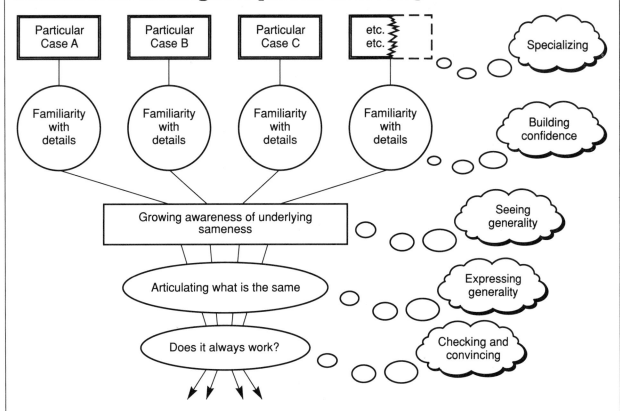

This model of the investigative process is a pictorial description of the way in which humans formulate concepts not just in mathematics but in any topic they attend to. It describes the processes you or pupils in your class went through when trying to formulate a view of the concept underpinning your recent investigations. If the stages are not too obvious in your recollections we suggest you try another investigation and evaluate the extent to which this model works for you.

If that *is* what you do when you work investigatively and *you* need all that time to work at lots of special cases, with plenty of opportunity to discuss with others what you and they understood, then three questions emerge.

1. *To what extent do you organise your classroom to permit such learning processes to take place in it?*

2. *To what extent do you and your colleagues work together using similar processes as you investigate your professional response to the art of learning and teaching?*

3. *To what extent do you and your colleagues explore investigatively your collective response to the issues raised, for example by TVEI or the National Curriculum, or even a recent HMI inspection of your school?*

2. INVESTIGATING ASPECTS OF TEACHING AND LEARNING

Consider again the work of the teacher group which is described in the case studies in Part V as an example of the three general points made above:

1. *In the third case study, the two teachers were able to make sameness and generalisation an overt consideration for the pupils who were working on the Pythagoras exercise.*

Thus the class were able to reach articulation of the underlying sameness of the various questions of the exercise, i.e. they were able to articulate Pythagoras' theorem for themselves. See the figure below for the model-diagram which captures this process.

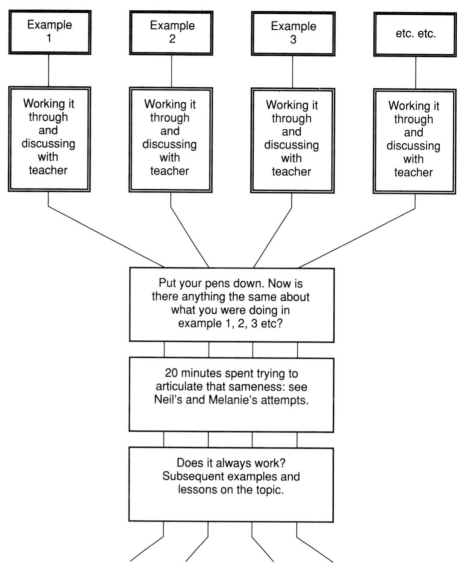

2. *The group of teachers, working together over several weeks were able to use anecdotes from members of their group and reach for the underlying issues which then became available for them when doing future work in their classrooms.*

3. *The teachers were addressing their concerns regarding particular attainment targets of the National Curriculum. For example, in the third case study it was A.T. 10, Shape and Space, level 7. As they shared anecdotes from their experiences in the classroom their general awareness of what the attainment targets might demand in terms of classroom work became clearer.*

This shows three different levels of application of the model: the first as applied to concept formation in syllabus topics; the second as applied to forming concepts regarding ways of working in the classroom; the third as applied to interpreting the National Curriculum attainment targets.

3. THE MODEL AS A GENERAL PROCESS

The essence of this model is that from a number of discrete special cases of *something* a deliberate seeking for the samenesses involved can lead to the identification of some general principle which can then be scrutinised and tested. In terms of doing mathematical investigations the special cases are likely to be particular mathematical instances from which a pattern might be seen and perhaps ultimately a general formula expressed. In terms of the anecdoting process, the special cases are the anecdotes. The seeking for sameness leads to questions about what the anecdotes have in common and the process of generalisation involves reaching for the issue or issues which underlie the anecdotes. The following diagram was given in Part IV, and it can be seen how this corresponds to the model-diagram on the last page.

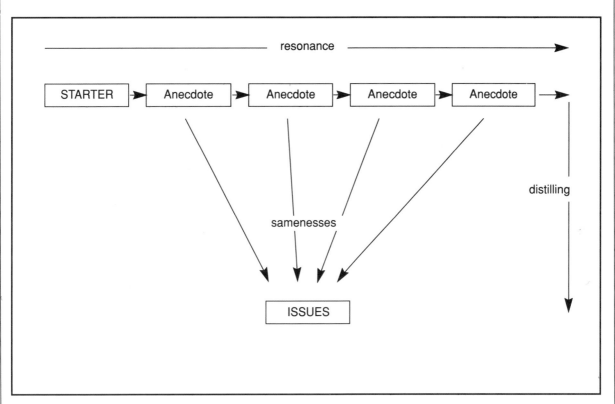

Thus the model of the investigative process encompasses not only mathematical investigation in the classrom but also the anecdoting process describing in Part IV, and exemplified throughout this pack. Even more powerfully it can also provide a way of regarding professional development and inservice events.

The model can in fact be seen to operate at yet a higher level. Consider the example of the two teachers working with pupils on the Pythagoras exercise, and subsequently reporting back to the group on their experience. If we regard this as example 1 of a series of examples of teachers applying the generalising process in their classroom to text-book exercises on syllabus topics, then we can see a set of examples from which the samenesses might be sought.

For example,

Case 1 – Generalising from questions in an exercise on Pythagoras theorem;

Case 2 – Generalising from questions in an exercise on solving equations;

Case 3 – Generalising from questions in an exercise on data handling;

Case 4 – Generalising from questions in an exercise on probability;

Case 5 – . . .

These cases could be all particular examples from the classroom of just one teacher, or they could be from various teachers providing that the experiences are shared through anecdotes and the group collectively work on the underlying issues. What is important is that through the various cases develops a growing awareness of what working this way in the classroom actually implies, what strategies are particularly useful, what teaching styles essentially appropriate. The result of such growing awareness is genuine professional development, an increasing of teaching wisdom by individual teachers and by the group as a whole.

4. PRACTICAL IMPLICATIONS OF THE THEORY

It is important to realise the power of the *successive* examples in allowing general awareness to be reached. One example alone, or even two, provide little experience from which to generalise and it would be unlikely that lasting benefit would accrue. You may recall in Parts II and V that we spoke of the importance of at least *three* experiences of the anecdoting process before a group of teachers could hope to come to an appreciation of what the process might offer. This has salutary implications for inservice events. The one-off professional development day, or half-day course has little chance of making a lasting contribution to genuine professional development. It alone, can do little more than seed a few ideas. If these ideas are not given sustenance and further opportunity to take root, they are likely to wither and die.

Opportunities for furthering professional development need to be on-going. The one-day event needs to be part of a programme of events and not just an end in itself. Not every event would or could take up a whole day, indeed this would be impractical. What is possible is to have weekly or fortnightly meetings of shorter duration, but with an agreed purpose and an on-going programme. The three case studies of Part V described such an on-going programme. The teachers met regularly. They shared experiences from their classrooms in the form of anecdotes. They perceived general issues which led to proposed classroom action. After further classroom experience they reported back to the group again. The particular events which we reported in Part V illustrated growth within the group. From initially fuzzy awareness of what expressing generality might mean, they came to a position of being able to spot occasions in the classroom when an overt recognition of the value of expressing generality would benefit pupils' understanding of a concept. This involved a very considerable shift of awareness, which would be unlikely to have been achieved without the on-going group work.

It is worth detailing their programme of events as one example of such a continuing development programme. It all began with one INSET day at which the department as a whole worked on the Open University's pack 'Expressing Generality'. After this day, individual teachers tried out aspects of the Expressing Generality pack in their classrooms, interspersed with department meetings at which they shared anecdotes of classroom experiences and worked together further on the pack. Using the model-diagram which we saw earlier, we have:

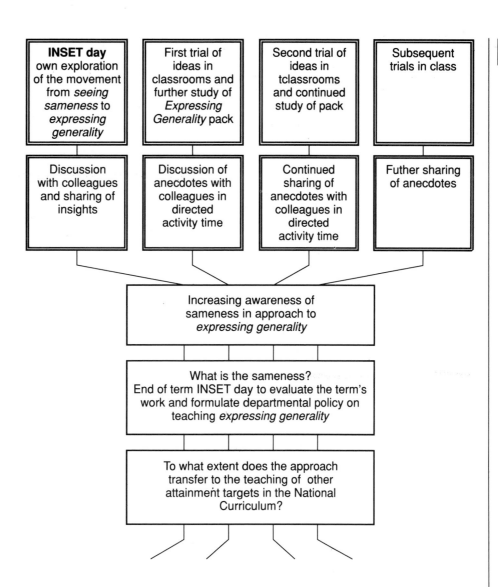

Looked at in this way, the INSET program devised by that maths department for *Expressing Generality* actually exemplifies a way of working at one's own professional development as well as that of one's colleagues. This was the subject behind Part II – *A way of working* and Part IV – *The anecdoting process*. Anecdoting is not just a quirky idea for having fun on INSET days. It is an integral part of a very purposeful plan for moving forward as a group of teachers – a whole staff actively involved in investigating ways and means of improving the learning and teaching in their school.

What is more the model described in this section gives substance to that *way of working*. It provides both the theoretical framework and a vocabulary for forms of staff development which are not of the one-off exposure type, nor even of a series of seemingly disconnected workshops.

5. THE IMPORTANCE OF DRAWING THE 'THREADS' TOGETHER

Before drawing the threads of the argument in this section together, take another look at the suggestion in Part II that a group of teachers would need to commit themselves to a minimum of three anecdoting sessions together before the full potential of the process could be appreciated.

The model of investigative processes was behind this suggestion too:

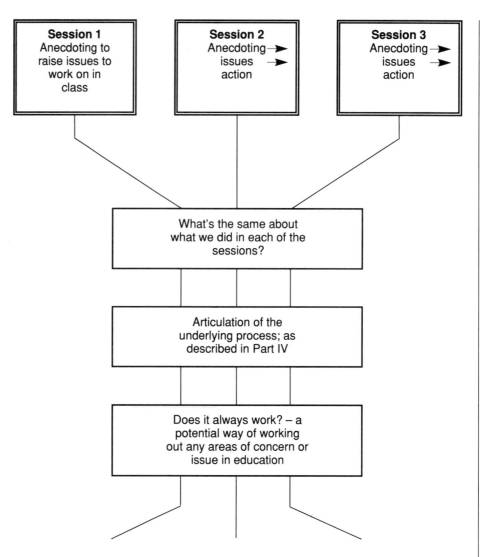

Not very much more needs to be said here. Look back over the three applications of the model discussed: teaching Pythagoras, working on Expressing Generality, and the session structure of Part IV . . . is there anything the same?! Can you say what that sameness is?

Apart from the fact that in each case, a minimum of three particular instances were investigated, the feature that stands out for us is the specific attention given to pulling the threads together. It was not left to chance that the learners in each situation would see the sameness and formulate some sort of concept of what underpinned the special cases they explored. *Time* was specifically given to the learners concerned – be they pupils or teachers – to articulate and, thereby, bring to the surface of their consciousness just what that underlying sameness was.

All too often, this is the stage that teachers and staff developers leave out or give scant time to, and yet, after specialising, expressing the underlying generalisation lies at the heart of all human learning. And, in the words of the teacher working on expressing generality, doing so is non-trivial.

The next stage, of course is to ask does it always work? Are you convinced of the validity of what you've found, and can you convince others? Working at finding the answers to these questions is what lies at the heart of all curriculum and professional development.

Well, does the model always work?

Applying the theory to a consideration of cross-curricular initiatives

We have suggested in Parts V and VI that the anecdoting process can be applied to general themes of interest or concern in order to enable participants to address these themes and develop their awareness of them. We have said moreover, that the anecdoting process is underpinned by a theory of sameness and generalisation which allows investigation within very diverse areas of concern at many levels.

The TVEI initiative has widely encouraged the relating of the entire curriculum to the 'world of work'. Indeed, a major contribution of TVEI to the secondary curriculum has been in encouraging cross-curricular initiatives which enable young people to relate what they learn in its widest sense to the world which surrounds them.

The secondary curriculum has traditionally been split into subject areas, and this has made linking across subject boundaries particularly difficult for the learner. In fact artificial boundaries have been introduced which have placed barriers in the way of what might be expected to have been natural linkages. Whereas the primary school curriculum makes it possible to explore general themes in relation to all the relevant subject areas, the secondary curriculum has traditionally inhibited this.

Using the model-diagram which has become familiar throughout this section we should like to suggest how the model might be applied to cross-curricular linking, and to accompany this with an anecdote from a mathematics teacher which suggests how the process might begin. The model-diagram may be seen below. It should be assumed that some concept is being explored which has manifestations in different subject areas. The exploration of the concept in each subject area provides the special cases from which sameness can be explored and a general concept developed which transcends any particular subject area.

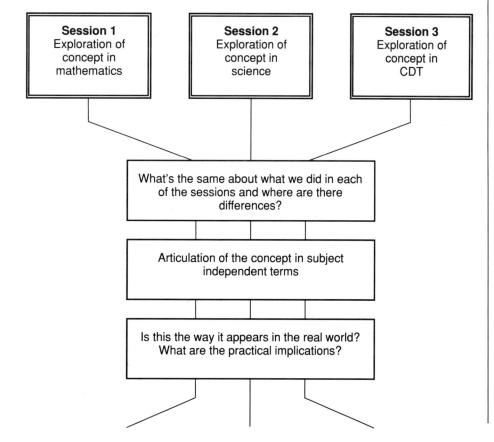

The following anecdote provides an example which illustrates this process:

Enlargement

I had been teaching the topic of enlargement to a third year group who seemed to be handling well ideas of centre of enlargement and scale factor. For example, taking the origin of rectangular axes as the centre of enlargement and a scale factor of 3, they could draw a starting shape, draw lines from the origin of its vertices, triple the length of these lines and finally draw the enlargement of the original shape:

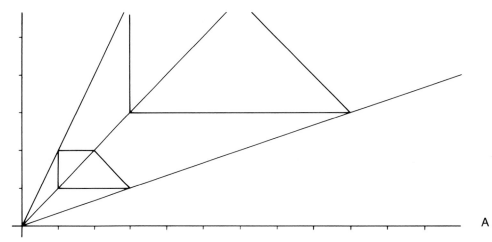

A

Before our lesson on a Wednesday afternoon they have art, and, one Wednesday, I happened to wander into their art lesson. To my surprise I saw the teacher trying to get them involved in something which looked familiar to me. It was perspective drawing. For a given vanishing point they were expected to produce a perspective drawing of a house. The teacher had a diagram up on the board which looked like the following:

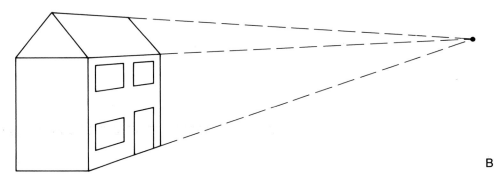

B

To me this was only very slightly different to what I had been asking them to do in mathematics.

To my considerable surprise, however, they were having tremendous difficulty. Looking around at individual efforts I could see drawings of houses with the weirdest perspectives. They just didn't seem to have got the idea. When I talked to the art teacher, he said that it was proving a real struggle.

So, when they subsequently came to Maths I asked what had been the difficulty. It became clear that the similarities which had seemed obvious to me were far from obvious to them. I got some very blank looks when I asked how they might use what they had learned about enlargement to enable them to succeed at perspective drawing.

So instead of enlarging just any old shape as we had been doing (like in A above), I suggested that we start with a square with a triangle on top, and enlarge that by a scale factor of 4 (see C below).

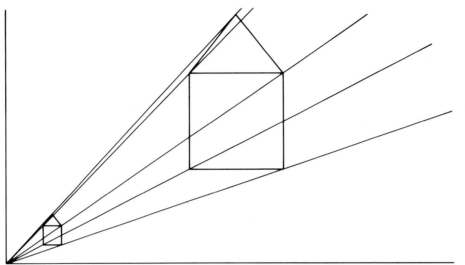

C

They had no problems with this, so I said, 'I wonder what happens if, instead of putting our starting shape in the first quadrant, we place it in the third or fourth quadrants?'

We did this on the board, for the square and triangle with a scale factor of 3, (see D below). Then, without saying anything, I rubbed out all the chalk lines except those which would leave a perspective drawing of two houses. I then filled in little windows and doors. Suddenly, 'Oh look!' filled the room, 'That's just like what we've been doing in Mr Thing-a-me's art lessons! It's easy!'

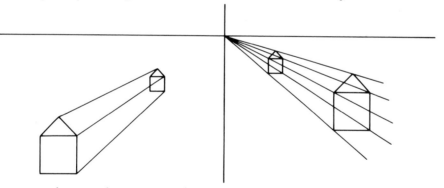

D

They got quite excited about it. Almost before I knew what was happening we were getting the most amazing perspective drawings. I particularly remember someone producing a perspective of tall buildings at the corner of a street, using two vanishing points, and one group of pupils jointly produced what looked like a perspective view of Manhattan using shapes in four quadrants. We put them all up on the walls which began to resemble the art room!

When we talked about the difficulties which they had had, they said that it had just never occurred to them to link what they were doing in art to something in maths. They were different subjects weren't they?

It was very salutary for me. I realised what artificial barriers we unintentionally created by compartmentalising the curriculum into such tight subject areas that pupils could not spot even the more obvious links.

It is quite common for pupils to meet mathematical ideas in other subject areas and to claim no recognition of the mathematics which the other-subject teacher wants to be used. Often this is because it is presented from a different point of view to the way they have seen it in a mathematics lesson, but too often the reason has more to do with the change of context. Too often, mathematical ideas are learned as if in a vaccum, bearing no relation to the world at large. So graphs in a science lesson, or statistical techniques in a social studies lesson seem to bear no resemblance to the abstract notions which have been presented in mathematics. This is not to suggest for a moment that the only purpose in doing mathematics is its utility value and that there should not be scope for the aesthetic pleasure of doing mathematics for its own sake. The world around us is not compartmentalised into subject areas. There is scope for seeing many aspects of a particular concept, for example abstract design, perspective drawing, mathematical enlargement, as parts of a whole experience. What is needed possibly, is for subject teachers to recognise links between the concepts which are offered to pupils and exploit these fully. The National Curriculum can help. A mathematician reading the science attainment targets will recognise many topics and processes which have close links to mathematics, and vice versa. The same must be true between many other pairs of subjects.

The substance of the diagram on page 105 could be realised by teachers exploring how they can support subject links by offering pupils explicit encouragement to see manifestations of a given concept in other subject areas. In this way pupils will be encouraged to learn in a holistic way which truly prepares them for the world around.

One might envisage on-going inservice sessions involving teachers from different subject areas, sharing anecdotes from their classrooms, drawing out the issues relating to cross-curricular work, going back into the classroom to try out new ideas and perceptions and generally developing their awareness of the curriculum as a whole.

VII

GETTING STARTED ON WORKING WITH COLLEAGUES

Part VII involves considerations of the reality for teachers of working together as part of their day to day professional work and development. In particular it considers how group sessions might work and sorts of action which might result.

Contents

Introduction

1. Incidental anecdoting – all in a school day

2. Cautionary tales – working on other people's issues

3. School-based INSET

Introduction

Part VII offers various anecdotes about anecdotes. Teachers in schools and advisory teachers give candid accounts of how they have used anecdotes in both formal and informal meetings, to raise issues amongst their colleagues. Some of these meetings seem much more successful than others! Reading about them may help to give you some idea of the many situations in which this style of working together is appropriate. It will also indicate some of the strengths and weaknesses teachers have found in using this approach.

Incidental anecdoting – all in a school day

1. IN THE STAFFROOM

It was lunch time in the staffroom when the question of who was on playground duty that afternoon arose. Great sympathy was offered to the unfortunate teacher whose turn it was:

'Yesterday afternoon was horrendous – fights all over the place!'

'It was the same on Tuesday afternoon. I seemed to spend all my time sorting out arguments over whose goalposts were whose.'

'My problem was the girls who spent most of the time falling out with one another. It continued in the classroom afterwards. I was certainly glad to see the back of them that afternoon!'

Similar anecdotes followed from the other teachers until the Head commented that all the incidents seemed to be happening in the afternoon. Perhaps it was this issue that needed discussion. On reflection the other teachers agreed that this was indeed the case and some explanations, such as the heat and the children being tired, were suggested. As time was limited, it was decided to make playtime an item on the agenda of the next staff meeting.

When the matter was discussed again it was generally felt that the children were tired by the afternoon and that the lack of shade added to the problem. There were no quick solutions to this last point (vandalism had prevented earlier attempts at tree planting) but it was decided that it might be better to stop having a playtime in the afternoon. This was agreed – many teachers commented that afternoon play was more of a disruption than a help. Many classes had some form of organised games during the afternon anyway, and each teacher was free to have an impromptu playtime if it seemed appropriate. This new arrangement was to be tried for a few weeks and, if successful, a more formal change would be made to reflect this in the school hours the following academic year.

2. THE END OF THE DAY

A teaching day, surrounded by children, students and parents can still be remarkably lonely. Isolation thrives within the detail of day to day survival. Sometimes it can seem as though the only time for discussing teaching and education is the staff group meetings that preceed term. Such meetings may raise all sorts of questions and issues, but when is there time for follow up work to reflect on classroom practice and progress? Year group meetings carry a heavy agenda; curriculum meetings are focused exclusively on assimilating the National Curriculum and it is taboo to 'talk shop' in the staffroom. One of the few times left to each of us is the end of the school day.

Often, once the last plimsoll has been found and the last child united with a parent, I work my way back to my own classroom via those of my immediate colleagues. This is a time for listening and sharing the minute triumphs and failures of the school day. Often one tired teacher tells another of the exasperation felt by certain children's behaviour: Elena has refused to speak to anyone all afternoon; Jeremy has destroyed an admirable piece of work because of a single error; Jo has not sat still for more than two minutes together; Lisa has been name calling again. . . . Sometimes strategies for tomorrow are discussed; sometimes a sympathetic murmur is comment enough – seldom are the stories used to consider more general concerns.

Last term, however, we were working as a staff on developing a policy for a particular curriculum area – art. Despite an excellent INSET day to raise issues and to practise some of the skills ourselves, within my year group the initiative seemed to be flagging. We were not confident enough in our own approach to art to believe we could teach it too! I decided to deflect the afternoon chat time to focus on the development of art rather than on behaviour. Sometimes I introduced anecdotes from my own classroom.

Art

```
Sam called me over to look at his bowl of fruit in chalk. I knelt
down and was looking over his shoulder. I wondered what to say about
it. I was impressed by what he had achieved but wondered if — and how
— I should push him further. Then he turned to me and said, 'I know
what you're going to say! You're going to say that the light from the
windows changes the colours on the bowl and that I could put it on my
bowl too!' And without waiting for my reply he leaned over for
another chalk . . .

I asked a group of children sketching to show the whole class what
they had done and tell us all any problems they had had and how they
had got over them. Every single child said, in his or her own way,
that it was looking at the object that had solved the problems.
```

Sometimes I had no stories to tell but focused instead on whatever was visible in the classroom: 'Which of those pictures are you most pleased with?' 'That's beautiful – did it take long?'

It didn't matter at all to me what issues were taken up. My overriding intention was that art should be discussed and that we should share the triumphs and tribulations of teaching it. It certainly helped us to keep up the momentum and to clarify where the real problems lay.

3. SWAPPING CLASSES

This term we have been considering the best use of our Science assessment sheet. It is a group sheet and requires a description of what happens in a group of children working on a given problem for a given time. The infant teacher had expressed worries about:

- having time to fill in the sheet during a session when every group needs her;
- being able to remember what happened after a session in order to write up the sheet;
- how much she should intervene, or stand back and watch, when a group gets stuck;
- differentiation within an activity.

Last week the infant and junior teachers swapped places to experience different age groups at work. This gave rise to several anecdotes, one of which follows.

Candles

It was the group measuring time using candles — they just could not see what to do. I asked masses of questions to try and make them think but they were completely stuck. In the end I suggested that they might use a felt-tipped pen to mark the candle in sections. After that they were away. No more difficulty understanding the problem! At the end William said, 'That wasn't a very good quality candle, was it?' indicating one of the variety of candles they had used. I still don't know if I was right to <u>tell them what to do</u>.

This one anecdote begins to address the infant teacher's worries about assessment and differentiation. Through it we might have gone on to explore:

- *how much time she spent with one group;*

- *how well she remembered the details two days later;*

- *how, by unwrapping a little of the activity, she had inspired the group to explore many more layers of the problem;*

- *how one child saw another problem ready to be tackled – did the quality of the candle affect its efficiency as a timing device? – thus showing that the children were working at a variety of levels.*

It is interesting to see that teachers' worries can be answered from their own experience!

We are going to evaluate our Science work in a forthcoming National Curriculum closure day. I hope to use this anecdote to generate others or else to begin with the question 'Can you think of an instance where your direct intervention has been vital, or obstructive, in an activity?' In either case I hope that using anecdotes from our own experience will boost our confidence as we begin to unwrap the assessment package of the National Curriculum.

Cautionary tales – working on other people's issues

1. EXTRACTING ISSUES

Having just been to a conference where I had experienced the power of anecdote to generate issues, I was very keen to 'have a go' the following Wednesday on one of the county's National Curriculum INSET days.

I had been asked to be a group leader, and in the next breath I was told that the two pyramids (High School and feeder Middle and Primaries) had been very awkward and obstructive at their first INSET day! With this encouragement, I set off determined to infiltrate at least a little of the approach I had so recently experienced.

The agenda had been organised by a High School teacher ('very inflexible and hard to get on with' – another comment to inspire!) who had been seconded to assess TVEI and INSET in the county. However, she was very pleasant and, although we followed her pattern, I was able to insert the Open University's 'Ball Rolling' video[1] as one option in the afternoon programme. I also decided to use the disciplined 1-2-4 approach to generate discussion on assessment in place of the perennial brainstorming session.

The teachers gathered at 9.30 a.m. My group had 15 members. Two were Middle School teachers and the rest Primary, including one from a Special School. We represented many different approaches to the classroom and to assessment.

'Before we fill in this flip chart sheet,' I began, 'I would like you to reflect for a few moments and jot down your main worries and concerns about assessment.' The group, who were a cheery and amenable lot, began and after a couple of minutes I felt it appropriate to move into the next phase.

'Before we share our ideas all together, spend some time talking to the person next to you, sharing what you have written.' There was no resistance to this idea and a lively interchange began which could have gone on for the whole of this first session. I took part too and had an interesting exchange of stories with a teacher from one of the Middle Schools. However, we needed to draw together our ideas and look for issues and, from my point of view, *samenesses*.

In the full group discussion everyone had something to say. There were a lot of worries. Although these worries seemed diverse, as anecdotes were used to illustrate points, it emerged that everyone's main concern was *time*! 'How do I spend enough time with one or two children?'

This issue of time and its supporting anecdotes pointed, I thought, to another 'sameness' more pertinent to the county's INSET programme: *classroom management*. However, when I gently suggested this, a lot of the teachers in the group became defensive – as though it was easier to look outside their own classroom practice and moan about large classes, the organisation of the school, the authority etc. than to begin to look for strategies to use within their existing organisation. The classroom, as one group leader had so rightly said at the earlier conference, is where issues 'really bite' and if practice is to change, teachers need to explore their own approaches to all aspects of the curriculum.

---

1 See Part II, section 3.

I was, and am, in no way being judgemental of my group of experienced and conscientious people. Perhaps the issues of classroom management should be explored in school, where the atmosphere is less threatening. Anyway, our flipchart sheet included 'classroom management' as well as 'time'! And the rest of the day unfolded without further noticeable feelings of unease or exposure.

2. WORKING AND NOT WORKING

I used a set of five written anecdotes on 'Girls and Technology' on a Mathematics and Computers course for Middle Years. It was the first time the group had met and they seemed cold towards each other. Reflecting and describing in pairs just fizzled out. When we tried to open up the discussion they complained that the 'political nature' of the material prevented them from exploring their own school situations. One teacher expressed anger that the writer wished to make an issue of *gender* at all. Another agreed – it didn't happen in their schools – and therefore the session was inappropriate. These responses came from two men in the group of ten teachers.

On reflection, perhaps it was wrong to use a specific issue, 'Gender in Education' with a group that had no experience of working together in this way. Somehow the directed nature of the five anecdotes focused too clearly on an aspect of education and this seemed to prevent any broadening of the discussion. Next time I'll vary the content of the anecdotes I present.

I used to feel worried in other sessions that, although I could recognise the 'sameness' of the concerns raised by group discussion, when trying to make these concerns explicit there was often little response. We would then mill around in confusion at my interruption before settling back into general discussion.

Perhaps there are small concerns and big concerns relevant to each group. It is often not the written starter or even the first few anecdotes from the group that work. These serve to raise the warmth of the discussion and, perhaps twenty minutes later, I become aware that someone has offered the right trigger for that particular group.

3. IT COULDN'T HAPPEN HERE!

I was working as a facilitator on an equal opportunities INSET day. The morning included a range of talks and a short workshop on defining the situation in one's own school. The afternoon included workshops on more specific issues. In some of these the teachers were asked to read prepared scenarios of school incidents and reflect on how they would respond to them immediately and in planning policies over a longer term. Possible issues of interest were listed under each scenario.

The packaged stories were carefully prepared. Each one was sensitively tuned to the issues of racial and sexual stereotyping. They were based on real life incidents and all age ranges were represented. We read through the sheets before the conference and all the local facilitators were impressed! The teachers too were 'chosen'. They had selected themselves to spend a Saturday developing a whole school approach to Equal Opportunities. So I was quite surprised at the consternation which broke out amongst individuals of the group I was working with when they read the scenarios!

> '*This couldn't happen in* our *school.*'
>
> '*It is not like that* here.*'
>
> '*Our children wouldn't react in that way.*'
>
> '*But there* aren't *any Afro-Caribbeans in this area.*'

Only one *group* responded instantly to the alien situation: 'We have never been called on to intervene in an incident like this. We wanted to work out how we would react:

how we *should* react if challenged. We also wondered whether we are, in fact, tacitly ignoring behaviour patterns which exist but are not spoken about!'

All the other groups were stumped and looked to me to facilitate! I suggested, 'Share an incident from your own experience which seems to you similar in some way to the one portrayed in the script or that raised any one of the issues listed.' There was a pause and then, tentatively at first, the situations were personalised, became real and resulted in some excellent work on challenging assumptions and exploring the hidden curriculum.

On reflection, perhaps the difficulty was that the scenarios told us nothing of the original teachers' responses. What did they actually think or feel or do? We were asked to superimpose our ways of working onto someone else's unique situation as though it were a general problem which we could solve, instead of using a specific problem we had ourselves solved (or shelved) and through it elucidating more general issues of concern.

School-based INSET

1. GETTING PERSONAL

We used the 'bead' anecdote described in Part II, section 2 to begin a staff meeting. We then discussed what we thought was happening in the reception class described. It did not give rise to further anecdotes but it did raise:

- *what is the purpose of an activity?*

- *why was the teacher asking follow-up questions at that time?*

On this second point one colleague thought the teacher might be testing previous experience and knowledge while another thought that the question was completely off the cuff and that the teacher had given up when she didn't ask it again.

Both these comments seemed to reveal underlying concerns for these two teachers, but they were expressed in a general hypothetical form – one teacher's fear that an open-ended approach is too woolly and does not help the teacher to assess what the children have learned, and another colleague's worry about the frustrations of working with Reception class children. I should have liked to push the teachers to offer specific anecdotes from their own classes which would have given substance to their worries or fears, and allowed us to address the issues through some agreed form of action.

However, like the teacher in the anecdote, I did not feel it was an appropriate time to pursue either concern – so we headed to the pub for lunch!

2. CURRICULUM DEVELOPMENT

We planned to extend the use of calculators throughout the school. We began with a full day for all staff discussing issues, exploring materials and making plans for the term's work. We also scheduled year group meetings in the following months to provide everyone with opportunities to review progress and reflect on what was happening in each class. Towards the end of term we intended to have children working with calculators at an open evening for parents.

As the work with calculators began in the classrooms, so the anecdotes started to be relayed in the staffroom. Most of them centred round surprising results achieved by children – or the results achieved by surprising children!

> *'You should have seen Cocky and Lam. They settled with the calculator but methodically checked every single result with counters! Ian was the only one to say straight off that nought was not the smallest number you could show.'*
>
> *'Katharine showed me something I did not know . . .'*
>
> *'Sarah's work was fascinating . . .'*
>
> *'Even Elvis wanted to try . . .'*

Later the year group meetings began but suddenly the talk about individual children disappeared. Conversations switched to the procedural – 'We haven't enough calculators . . .' or to the minutiae of the lesson plan – 'We just tried that game about . . .'. It was a wrench to get *back* to the personal qualities of the anecdotes so freely shared in the staffroom earlier. Yet this seemed the single most apt way to get beyond the defensiveness '*We only* . . .', 'We couldn't *because* . . .', 'There's not enough time to . . .', to the issues of what we *could* achieve through using calculators in a planned way. I prompted my colleagues to share their stories once more. Sometimes I reminded them of something I'd already heard them say in the staffroom – 'Didn't you say Elvis achieved something interesting?' Otherwise I probed more generally, 'Did anyone in your class surprise you in what she or he achieved?' Prompting by name was a risk: a teacher who didn't respond to the cue would ask me for more details! If you are going to reflect other people's anecdotes back to them at a later date make sure you remember them fairly accurately!

Once the anecdotes were flowing, I felt a strong pressure to crystallise the issues and keep these always to the fore. A meeting over assembly time is not leisured. To work through any antipathy of being there – defensiveness in front of an 'expert', the need to generate stories and listen to them – to the position where issues can be clarified, worked on and used to indicate the way ahead, is no easy matter in 20 minutes!

The pace of work possible depends so much on the rapport already developed within any group. A team of teachers who are working together as, for example, a year group or a curriculum development group, is likely to reach a point of consensus long before a wary group which has never worked together before. One way I found effective in speeding the process was to begin by sharing two pieces of children's work. Briefly I outlined the task set and then showed the very different achievements of the two children. I personalised the sheets of work with a vignette of each of the children and retold what both of them had said to me. Even if these particular children were not known to the teachers, everyone could readily admit to having certain similar *types* of children in their classes. And then their own stories began to unfold . . .

VIII

ANECDOTES AND OTHER RESOURCES

Part VIII contains an anthology of anecdotes, collected from teachers and others, which might be used as starters for discussion.

It also includes information about other materials in various media which are referenced in the pack.

Contents

Introduction

An anecdote is someone's story. In the process of writing this pack we generated and collected many anecdotes related to many different themes. They all came spontaneously from people, many from teachers. They are presented as closely as possible to the way they were told without attempts to polish or refine them. We also make no judgements – they are just stories! In presenting them as a collection like this they lose the context in which they were originally offered which may be seen to deny possibilities of seeking *sameness* in reaching for underlying issues.

However, their purpose is not to inform or to exemplify, it is rather to spark resonance. If you read an anecdote which in some sense seems to 'speak to your experience' then pause to reflect on this. Just what is it that you recognise? Can you recall any incidents from your own experience which relate to the anecdote which you have read? If you can, then you are in a position to start looking for issues which underlie your response and recognition; you can develop your own awareness and you can be in a better position to take action in your professional life.

Another use for these anecdotes is to form *starters* for sessions with colleagues. In Part II we reported on sessions which used written anecdotes as a starter for discussion, and you may like to refer to these accounts for examples of how such a session might begin. You could choose a number of anecdotes which seem to relate to a particular theme, or simply some anecdotes which seem to you to have particular potency. In some cases just one anecdote could have the power to stimulate a group of teachers to produce many further anecdotes of their own from which issues could be distilled. The process of starting with anecdotes and seeking for issues which can lead to classroom action is exemplified in Part II and abstracted in Part IV. Parts V, VI and VII move towards the use of this process as part of a teacher's professional life.

The anecdotes each have a title, chosen to identify the anecdote rather than to label it. Some are organised into groups according to general themes. We would emphasise, however, that the meaning behind an anecdote will vary according to people's response to it, so you should make decisions yourself about which anecdotes are in some way related according to your own perceptions of them rather than according to our grouping.

It interested us that although we were chiefly mathematics educators, the anecdotes which sparked resonance and spoke powerfully to aspects of teaching and learning often had little to do with mathematics *per se*. Important issues which we ourselves related to the mathematics classroom could arise from anecdotes which were seemingly unrelated to the teaching and learning of mathematics. It seemed to us that we gained immensely from a wider perspective of education and issues arising from this. We have included a number of anecdotes relating to this wider perspective since they have potential to raise issues which are as potent for the mathematics classroom as those arising from anecdotes which have a more obvious relevance.

PART VIII

Some anecdotes

THE CLASSROOM

We actually got it right miss!

We were planning a school day trip with third and fourth year children. The children got so involved in the details of the planning that they wanted to extend the trip which eventually became a 3-day one; the children went to the shops and bought all the provisions they needed for the trip and they then went on the trip. At the end of it a child came to me and said, 'We actually got it right miss.' That comment made me suddenly realise that because those children had been completely involved in the planning they had no need for the teacher's tick, they knew they had got it right because it worked. It made me think about my role as a teacher and wonder whether the more usual way of doing things was likely to be so productive.

Mental magic

I always tried to get my mental arithmetic through dinner money and so I always involved the children in it. I used to count it all on my fingers to be sure I'd got it right, because I was trying to keep so much in my head at the same time. Then one day I noticed that one of the children had just produced the answer from her head. I asked her how she'd done it. She indicated that she knew two sixes were twelve so for six and seven she just added one more. I was amazed that she had thought of a method for herself.

The excitement of learning

I was working with a reception class who were using Cuisenaire rods to make ten by matching the ten rod in different ways. As I watched the children matching up two fives and five twos etc., I suddenly appreciated for the first time the relationships there are between the four operations: $+$, $-$, $\times$, $-$. I was <u>so</u> excited and it made me think how exciting it must be for children when they realise about something.

The effect of success

I had a child with language problems which often prevented him from
communicating adequately with me and with the other children.
Basically he was a slow learner. One day we were doing an activity
which he did quite quickly and which he wanted to share with the
other children. He suddenly realised that he didn't always have to be
the one who was helped by the others and that he had something to
offer other children. He's flourished after that. It changed his
relationship with me and with the rest of the class.

Complacency

I used to go into one school in an advisory capacity and so did not
know the children so well. I thought I'd use an activity with numbers
that I'd used successfully in other classes. It involved giving all
the children a number and asking them to make up a group with all the
other children holding a number that related to their number in some
way. Nothing happened. I didn't know how to get them started and I
had feelings of panic about an activity that had gone so well with
other classes. I tried asking leading questions about how to start
and what to do. Eventually a child said, 'I think we need to know
what other people have got,' but even then they didn't start until
one child said, 'Oh, can we get up?' After that they moved around and
talked and found their groups. It was the lack of success with a
usually successful activity which set me wondering about how we can
get to feel complacent about things which have always gone right
before.

Confidence

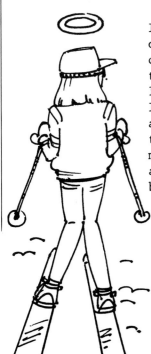

I was learning to ski; I did very well at first and got
quite confident but one day I had a bad fall and
completely lost my confidence. For a while I wouldn't
try at all and eventually the instructor asked me if I'd
like to go back to the beginners class for a while.
I did. I then did all the things that I knew I could do
all over again and it gave me back my confidence to try
the other things again. It made me think of children in
my class who get despondent from failing at what they
are doing and I thought we should always let them go
back for a time to things they know they can do.

Standing back

We were using LOGO. The children were in pairs working on shapes with a computer near by. Two children were using the computer and eventually all the rest of them were drawn to where these two were working. They began to discuss it as a group and were helping each other to understand. I felt a great urge to intervene but I made a determined effort to stand back and just listen. It was amazing what they were learning from each other.

Fun together

When my class came up to me they hadn't been used to sharing mathematics so I was trying to encourage them to work together. At first they were quite inhibited about it and I kept saying, 'Oh this is fun isn't it?' The other day when I was starting something off a little boy came up to me and said, 'Is this going to be fun miss?' And what he meant was 'Are we going to work together?' I realised that working in isolation had got him into a panic and he needed the support of working together.

Imagery

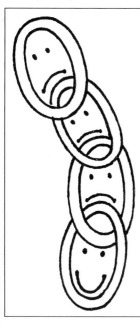

I find it difficult to teach art! One day I was watching a skilled teacher of art working with some seven-year-old children who were drawing chains. The inevitable happened. After the first few careful links, each new link overlapped the last but did not interlock. How would my colleagues save the sketch? I crept closer to listen: 'Look at the chain you have drawn. Imagine you are going to pick it up. Take hold of one link and lift it off the paper . . .' The child's eyes grew wide in horror. 'It just falls apart!' he cried.

My colleague's gentle question, allowing both teacher and pupil to enter the child's imaginative world, would have come easily to me in a <u>mathematical</u> investigation — but I had never thought it appropriate in sketching where a child's response seemed simply right or wrong.

Jaime

Jaime is not usually the pupil with the answers. He can add 5 and 7 and still get it wrong. So when I introduced the group to problem solving with the handshake problem I was surprised when, a few minutes later, Jaime said he'd done it. What he actually said was that he hadn't got an answer but he'd done it all the same. I asked him to explain. 'It's easy,' he said, 'I've got to shake everyone's hand, except my own, of course, so that's 26. Then Steven here, he's got to shake everyone's hand too but he's already shaken mine, so that's 25. It's the same for each of us. So all you have to do is add up 26 and 25 and 24 all the way to . . . If you give me a calculator, I can tell you the answer!'

Number lines

Leanne was completing a workcard. Using a printed number line she methodically counted back to answer the first five questions:

3 less than 7 is ___

7 less than 7 is ___

2 less than 7 is ___ etc.

The last answer she filled in without a pause:

4 less than 7 is ___

I asked her how she had done that so quickly. 'It's easy,' she replied. 'It's one more less than the first one, so the answer is one more less too.'

Pupil initiative

When as a pupil you have a problem at school you often feel really isolated . . . as if no-one else can feel the way you do. And if you put your hand up in class to ask a question you feel really daft. I was having a real problem with my maths because the teacher spoke so quickly I couldn't keep up. In the end I mentioned it to my best friend . . . and she said she had exactly the same problem. So we decided that in the next maths lesson we wouldn't do any writing. When the teacher noticed us he asked why we weren't working. We told him he spoke too fast for us to keep up. Instead of going mad he told us he'd never realised he spoke so quickly and thanked us for telling him! Things are much better now.

Mathematics investigations

I have a bank of mathematics problems and investigations in my classroom and children are free to choose any which appeal to them. The difficulty I face however, is at what point do I intervene when children are 'off course'. One example is the 'crossing the desert' problem (<u>Thinking Things Through</u> — Leone Burton, 1984). I cannot recall the exact problem, but 'two men have a message to deliver across a desert. They each have six days supply of food but it would take nine days to cross the desert. Can they deliver the message?'

I find that children often try to change the question, e.g. kill one man, come across an oasis, etc. but having ruled these questions out, how long should they be left to puzzle before giving clues?

There <u>is</u> an answer to this particular problem, and I feel that in my efforts not to give too much direction, I leave the children a little too long trying to puzzle out how the message can be delivered.

On the other hand, I follow the TV programme 'Landmarks' with my class. One session of this was devoted to container lorries and ships. After the broadcast the children were asked (from a Landmarks worksheet) to place a number of containers on ships according to their weight, e.g. heaviest on the bottom level, lightest at the top level. Having done this, we decided that we ought to 'balance' these containers so that the ship would be safe to travel. There were four rows of containers, heavy, moderately heavy, medium and light, and four containers in each category. Once started on the task the children soon discovered that there were a number of ways in which the ship could be loaded to balance it.

In this investigation, because I was as unsure of the outcome as the children (or almost!) there was no conflict regarding intervention — we all worked on it together!!

Loss of control

Secondary School 11–16. First year class involved in new pilot material for SMP 11–16. Children all busy and engaged. Hum of activity. Teacher standing by desk looking miserable. On questioning it transpired that her enjoyment in teaching was derived almost entirely from performing the role of controller and provider of learning. It was, for her, an acting and a power role. The fact that the children were learning was not important. She did not want to be a manager of learning.

Priorities

We were planning a school INSET programme on maths. First we
brainstormed the matter and ended up with a list of issues that
concerned us. Then we tried to prioritise the issues by voting: each
member of staff gave three votes to the issue of greatest concern,
etc. (We have worked like this before on other curriculum areas and
reached a good level of consensus.) What happened with the maths was
that I was the only person to vote for the calculator issue. No-one
else was concerned about it at all. As maths coordinator, I felt
frustrated that no one else felt that calculator use even <u>was</u> an
issue!

Divisibility by 4

During the course of a session with a group of teachers, we looked at
an eleven-year-old's account of her search to find a quick test of
divisibility by 4. Amongst the skills and processes demonstrated
were specialising forming an hypothesis, checking, generalising and
division. One of the first comments was 'Why hasn't a calculator been
used?' A sharp intake of breath was heard from another member of
staff. At a later stage of the same discussion, the teacher who had
displayed unease at the thought of a calculator being used, said
forcefully, 'She should know the test already. Why hasn't she been
told it?' My immediate unspoken reaction was that I had gained A-
level maths and taught the subject for 11 years to A-level without
knowing the test for divisibility by 4 and had only discovered it
through reading this piece of work.

Ownership

I recently had to trial some INSET materials with a
group of teachers. Although I read the material several
times, it was not part of me when I came together with
the group. I found I needed the book as a prompt and the
session began rather stiltedly. The group reacted
strongly and changed the session to a more practical one
which lead to profitable discussion and a selective use
of the materials. The session had group ownership now
and I felt part of it, not its controller, a much better
feeling — I hope from all participants.

That's my subject

I recently attended a meeting about Geography in the National Curriculum. The other members of the group represented schools from all age phases. Quite an argument developed between some of the secondary teachers about which subject area — mathematics, science, humanities — could, or should, teach certain topics. The primary teachers looked on in amazement!

Computer problems

A group of teachers were discussing computer use in their schools. 'Well,' one of them said, 'it used to be okay when we had stand-alone machines, but now all the computers are networked. I just don't know how it all works and before you can do anything you have to ask the expert. It takes a long time to retrieve procedures. We have to do funny things and things get lost. I now have stopped using the computer at all in my lessons because it all seems too much of a problem and also too much of a mystification.' Another teacher agreed and added, 'The person in charge of the network doesn't seem to want to share the knowledge.'

THOUGHTS ON GENDER

The expert

The scene is in the computer laboratory of a college of education where some teachers are following an inservice course on using the computer. The class is being taken by a very enthusiastic, very competent male lecturer. He shows a great amount of software. Each piece of software is shown very swiftly, slickly even. As time ticks by, more and more of the teachers, particularly the women, are looking bemused and bewildered. The lecturer seems unaware of this. He continues showing the amazing pieces of software, showing the amazing things that the software can do — the colours, the graphics. Eventually the teachers move to the machines and try some of the software themselves. The lecturer circulates around. He continually intervenes and takes over the machines himself. He leans over, types, speaks quickly and shows them what key to press for the next amazing effect.

Computer-mania

The bell has gone and the computer room starts filling up with
pupils, all boys. The boys come in with their bags over their
shoulders. They immediately dive for the machines and start working
furiously — either programming in BASIC or playing with the latest
computer game. The atmosphere is completely male, male jokes, male
aggression. One girl puts her head around the door, sees all the boys
inside and leaves quickly.

Panic

Two girls are working with LOGO and have just defined a recursive
procedure. They do not know that it will 'go on forever' unless they
find a way to stop it in the procedure. They become completely
horrified as the picture continues and continues. Panic stricken
they switch off the monitor to the computer assuming that if they
cannot see it the program must have stopped.

Doing the typing

Our group was mixed boys and girls. We had to produce a project but I
don't think that any of the boys in our group could type quickly so
the girls took this on. If one of us boys had attempted to do this it
would have been a hindrance . . . it was simply a case of who was
good at typing so that we could get on quicker. It wasn't a case of
getting the girls to type . . . it wasn't meant to be sexist.

Fractal man

A group of adults are discussing a recent television programme about
chaos. One of them says, 'There were some amazing computer graphics
about fractals. It certainly is such an exciting visual and
intriguing subject — but why was every presentation made by a man?'

The chippy *man's* charter?

Wherever there is change, perceptions vary, and it may be the case that the bigger the initiative, the wider the variation.

At the time of this anecdote, TVEI (the Technical & Vocational Education Initiative) had been underway for about a term. Its introduction had been rather sudden, but by now most of our staff were aware of its emphasis on new technology and had recently been alerted to its concern about gender stereotyping.

Year 10 options were in the offing and prospectuses were being prepared with a view to recruiting a 'cohort' of 150 TVEI students for the following year.

The advent of TVEI had been welcomed by the C.D.T. Department and seen as a timely recognition both of the importance of their role in a modern curriculum and of the expensive nature of their line of teaching.

One might imagine how the TVEI's initiators might have reacted if they had heard our Head of C.D.T. commenting: 'I'm going to need an awful lot of materials if there are going to be 150 boys doing woodwork next year.'

THE WORLD OF WORK

Work experience

When I did my work experience I did it at a newsagents and they didn't give me anything to do . . . and I hated going because nobody was friendly . . . and if that had been a real job I wouldn't have stayed there.

In my work experience I went to a bank. Everyone seemed surprised to see me when I turned up . . . They stuck me in a little office and I sorted cheques all the time, apart from the last two days when someone said maybe I'd better go to Standing Orders. I don't think I learned much about banking.

Well, I went to a solicitors and they made me feel very welcome. They introduced me and said I'd come to do work experience. I didn't get <u>much</u> experience of a solicitors' office but they were very friendly to me. There was one man who came in twice a week and he said he'd try and get me to court if there was a chance . . . and he let me sit in on some of his interviews . . . he involved me and I really enjoyed it there. They even gave me a key to the office at lunchtime — they really trusted me. I really enjoyed it and I've gone back and worked there in the holidays.

I worked with my dad . . . he's a builder and I really enjoyed helping him out. I've done it for seven years or more now . . . It gets me out and about in the fresh air, meeting people . . . and when I'm out working with him it's not like father and son but like mates.

In the school I went to they treated me like an adult, just like another member of staff. The only thing they wouldn't let me do was go in the staff room. They were really upset about that but they said it was the only time teachers had to let off steam . . . I felt really involved and was surprised they accepted me so much. I wasn't only pleased with the way they treated me, I found the work interesting as well.

I worked in an architects' office. It wasn't something I really wanted to do because I wasn't particularly interested in it as a career. I wanted to prove to myself I really didn't want to do it . . . I'm more interested in the 'arty' side. I did it because I thought it'll be an experience . . . and I did enjoy it. But from that I don't want to do it as a career — so it was beneficial.

Differing perceptions

A major national company was setting up a new undertaking in an area in which a secondary school was seeking industrial support for an ambitious project.

The company's manager invited a representative from the school to discuss the possibilities of their helping with the project. The discussions appeared to go very well.

The manager was encouraged to discover that there were several ways in which the company might make itself helpful, but assumed that he and the teacher were discussing a range of options.

The teacher was also encouraged by the company's ability to help, but was tending to assume that each new suggestion was extending the dimensions of a possible bonanza.

They parted on excellent terms, feeling that they had given the matter a good airing.

Later, at the school, there was some hesitation at the point of making a formal proposal to the company when it was calculated that the value of the entire range of help sought would run comfortably into four figures.

Nevertheless, the school took the plunge and asked for everything that had been discussed at the exploratory meeting.

Just how the manager reacted to the arrival of the letter is not recorded, but its impact was such that in the end the company made no contribution to the project whatsoever.

A complex subject

Subject teaching in secondary schools tends to give one a fairly compartmentalised view of one's students and of their capabilities.

When TVEI reached the 6th Form, enterprise activities were introduced with competing teams planning to set up potential businesses.

Inevitably, problems arose from the need to find time to accommodate such TVEI elements in the curriculum. The additional funding was welcome, but the loss of teaching time for straight A-levels was another matter.

One incident may serve to illustrate both the general and the specific difficulties.

It was planned to extract the student teams for 30 minutes apiece from normal lessons to present their business ideas to visiting bankers. This prompted the following exchange in the staff room.

HEAD OF MATHS 'Is it really essential for a first rate mathematician like Jane Doe to be involved in this exercise?'

TVEI CO-ORDINATOR 'Yes. It is essential for a first rate geographer like Jane to be involved.'

Despite such altercations, time was found for the entire enterprise programme and Jane made an excellent contribution to her team's efforts. But it may be significant that feedback from the other team members indicated that what they valued most about Jane were her skills as a diplomat and her talent as a graphic artist.

Preparations *versus serendipity*

It is a cardinal rule of fieldwork to check your sites before you actually visit them with a group of students.

Nevertheless, I reckoned that it would be fairly safe to assume that there would not be much change in the site of a Bronze Age settlement which I had surveyed several times before, and since its location was on Dartmoor, I persuaded myself that the negative expenses involved in checking it would not be worth incurring.

What I had overlooked was the change of season compared with all previous trips, and I·was dismayed on reaching the usual vantage point on the opposite hillside to discover that the previously splendid view of the layout of the settlement and its field system was no longer available, since two thirds of it were now obscured by bracken.

We were supposed to be sketching the layout from the vantage point and identifying target areas for further inspection, and it was the con artist rather than the teacher in me who suddenly switched the emphasis to speculation as to what mysteries might lie shrouded in that vegetation.

The teacher in me had plenty of time to regret the failure to incur those negative expenses as we crossed the valley and climbed the Bronze Age slopes. But the Moor has a magic of its own and it was not long before our students were spontaneously colonising the settlement, discovering huts, making them recognisable, laying claim to neighbouring fields and fighting off invaders.

Before long we had 'owners' for all the items of Bronze Age real estate that I had hoped to see recorded on their sketch maps, and the maps turned out to be the best ever, since they were all keen to share their discoveries with each other.

Perhaps we should let a little serendipity creep into the expense account from time to time.

What's the benefit?

My company was quite prepared to cooperate with the school in their TVEI project even though it meant showing several groups of pupils around the workplace and getting staff to explain what they do here.

The pupils who came appeared to fall into at least two distinct groups. Firstly there were those who looked seriously interested in the task set — they had notebooks and cameras at the ready. Other groups seemed ready to giggle, chat to their friends and totally lack the serious intent of the former. It was obvious from the start which groups would produce something worthwhile and I should think it is questionable whether some of the pupils benefited at all.

Who wants to know?

Ours is a company which works almost exclusively for the education service and our staff of technical and clerical officers and teachers is used to dealing with teachers at first hand.

When a local school approached us to see if we would be prepared to act as the subject of a mock 'take-over' for a sixth form business enterprise project we agreed to help.

Funnily enough though, when the students arrived and began asking questions about the running of various departments, some of our staff became quite anxious — even hostile.

Enterprise

I was in a meeting with a group of people interested in promoting the Arts in our local community. We were trying to think of ways of raising funding for a tour by a professional theatre company. Someone suggested commercial sponsorship — which sounded great in theory — but we doubted we'd have much success. Then one of our number chipped in:

'Let me tell you an anecdote. The Council for which I work has recently been involved in a joint project with the College of Higher Education in providing short courses for women returners. We were hopeful that the Training Agency would give us some money towards this but at the last minute we heard they couldn't fund us. In order to save the project we therefore had to find two lots of £250 from commercial sponsorship very quickly. By making a list of those companies with whom we had any form of contact, and working through it methodically by telephone, we managed to get the money we needed. And we found using the 'phone to approach companies much more successful because at least we were assured of talking to the person responsible.'

As a result of this timely anecdote we were spurred into action — it suddenly seemed possible that we might be equally successful.

The helpful bit

When we went to see the company we felt that some of the people
didn't want us — didn't seem to know what was going on . . . I know
they were busy . . . But one man who said he didn't come in very
often was really helpful. He was telling us all about the machines
and everything. He seemed to know what we wanted and said, 'These are
our problems, this is what we want solving. Have you any questions?'
We could <u>ask</u> him instead of him going on and on about things that
were completely irrelevant to us. In other places we took loads and
loads of notes . . . and we didn't even look at them. I wrote them
down just in case!

Fact or fiction?

As an amateur entertainer, my father used to tell a shaggy dog story
about a country bumpkin who was found with a horse-drawn barge and a
hammer and chisel, cutting two little grooves in the underside of one
of the bridges on the Bridgwater canal, just above the towpath.

When challenged by the village bobby, he explained that his horse was
too tall and he was cutting the grooves so that its ears could get
under the bridge.

The bobby told him not to waste his time and offered to lend him a
spade to dig out a few inches of the towpath instead.

'Don't be stupid,' the yokel replied. 'It's his ears as won't go
through, not his feet!'

Some years later, a particularly responsive class got me exchanging
observations about some of the less obvious features of the
industrial archaeology of canals. They told me what they had seen
which prompted me to mention similar things which they might look out
for.

The discussion had gathered momentum via mile posts, side ponds,
linesman's cottages, tunnel mouths, ventilation shafts, slots for
coffer dams, etc. etc., when someone mentioned ropemarks on
stonework and I suddenly caught myself saying, '. . . and sometimes,
on the undersides of bridges, you can find two little grooves where
. . . OOOOOPS!'

Other resources

Throughout the pack there have been references to various sources which in some way relate to or support the material of the pack. These are grouped together under appropriate headings below.

1. VIDEO MATERIAL

Working Mathematically with Infants – Open University
This includes the ball-rolling sequence described in Part II, section 3.

Working with Videotape of a mathematics classroom – Open University
This shows a group of teachers working on excerpts from videotape of their *own* classrooms in a manner similar to that described in Part II.

The Open University produces various classroom videotapes which are useful for the purposes described in this pack.

Details of these may be obtained from The Centre for Mathematics Education, The Open University, Milton Keynes MK7 6AA (Telephone number 0908 653550).

2. TEXTS

These are organised according to the part of the pack from which they are referenced:
Part II Section 2
Jaworski, Barbara, 'Investigating your own teaching', Unit 5 of ME234, *Using Mathematical Thinking* – Open University (1989).
[A further source of anecdotes. Obtainable from the Open University address given in (1) above.]

Part II Section 3
DES, *Mathematics Counts* (The Cockcroft Report) – London: HMSO (1982).

Part III
The following texts relate to *group work*:
Bedfordshire TMRS, *Training Manual for Schools. Key stage 3* (obtainable from Teaching Media Resource Service, Russell House, Ampthill, Beds).

Douglas, T., *Groupwork Practice* – London: Methuen (1976).

Easen, Patrick, *Making School Centred INSET work* – Open University/Croom Helm (1985).

Gattegno, Caleb, *The Commonsense of Teaching* – Educational Solutions (1974) (obtainable from Educational Solutions (UK) Ltd., 11 Crown Street, Reading, Berks).

Hare, A. P., *Handbook of Small Group Research* – New York: Free Press (1962).

Satow, Antoinette and Evans, Martin, *Working with Groups* – HEC/TACADE (1983) (obtainable from TACADE, 3rd Floor, Furness House, Trafford Road, Salford M5 2XJ).

Sturgess, David, *Working Together* – ATM (1988) (obtainable from ATM, 7 Shaftesbury Street, Derby DE3 8YB).

Part IV Section 3
ATM, *Teacher as Researcher* (1987) (obtainable from ATM, 7 Shaftesbury Street, Derby DE3 8YB).

Part V Section 2
Mason, John, *Expressing Generality* – Open University (1989).
[Obtainable from the Open University address given in (1) above.]

Part VIII Section 1
Burton, Leone, *Thinking Things Through* – Basil Blackwell (1984).

3. PROJECTS AND PACKS

These are referenced from Part V, section 2.

PrIME, standing for Primary Initiatives in Mathematics Education, is a major national project which at the time of publication of this document is in its second phase. An INSET pack has been produced, consisting of a file of 8 units, including about a hundred suggested activities for teachers on aspects of primary mathematics. It is published as follows:

Hilary Shuard, Angela Walsh, Jeffrey Goodwin and Valerie Worcester, *PrIME – Children, Mathematics and Learning*, Simon and Schuster, 1990.

CAN, standing for Calculator Aware Number, is a project within PrIME. Items relating to CAN, currently in press, are a book and associated video tape under the general heading of 'PrIME: Calculators, Children and Mathematics' to be published by Simon and Schuster.

Information on all of these materials can be obtained from Hilary Shuard, Homerton College, Hills Road, Cambridge CB2 2PH.

WE RAN TWO CONFERENCES . . .

This contains details of the conferences at which views of teachers were sought regarding the anecdoting process and associated way of working. A conference programme is included.

We ran two conferences

We ran two conferences which had important differences and similarities. They both had the same overall purpose which was to try out with teachers a way of working which we as a group had experienced ourselves, and which we believed had power to be valuable to teachers more widely in aiding professional development. We wanted to find out how the teachers responded to it, and hear their views on what we offered.

The first conference was held in Cumbria in February 1988, with our team and 16 teachers invited from primary and secondary schools by Geoffrey Faux, the mathematics adviser.

The second conference was held in Suffolk in February 1989, with our team and 45 primary and secondary teachers, 30 from Suffolk, invited by Peter Reynolds, the others from Hertfordshire, Bedfordshire and Cambridgeshire, invited by their respective mathematics advisers.

THE DIFFERENCE IN NUMBERS

One very obvious difference involved the number of people at each conference – 22 in Cumbria, 54 in Suffolk.

In retrospect it was important that the Cumbria conference was small. We were, at that stage, less confident about our ideas and the small numbers meant that we could work with groups of four teachers and get very close feedback from them. We were all able to fit into one large room, so even in small groups it was possible to have a sense of how everyone else was working. It was also possible to gather the entire conference together for discussion and everyone could listen and respond to everyone else. In our group, we were still relatively unfamiliar with working with each other at this stage and so it was reassuring to be able to see each other in operation.

In Suffolk, each member of the team had a group of seven or eight teachers, and it was not possible to work in such close proximity as in Cumbria. It was difficult to convene in plenary with any hope of whole group discussion. We were therefore dependent on having a fairly consistent and coherent story as group leaders, but we had learned from Cumbria, our ideas were much clearer and we ourselves were much more confident about *how* we wanted to work and *why*. The larger number of teachers meant that we had some very diverse views and experiences and could learn from interaction with these.

SIMILARITY OF STRUCTURE

Each conference began on Friday evening and continued until Sunday lunchtime, and we planned the sessions for Suffolk to correspond fairly closely to those we held in Cumbria so that comparisons could be made. The opening session on Friday evening was in each case an activity designed to focus attention on aspects of group working. The activity called 'Win as much as you can' (Eason 1985), is designed to offer the opportunity to explore elements in the tension between competitive and cooperative working. It raises issues about group leadership and communication. In both cases there were very strong reactions to it, and it seemed to serve its purpose well, although some participants dismissed it as a game.

We designed the three following sessions to take a similar form, that of working on anecdotes and raising issues. Each session had a different starter – in Cumbria we used *video*, *audio* and *personal* anecdotes as starters, and in Suffolk we substituted *written* anecdotes for the audio. One reason for this was that the quality of the audio anecdotes used in Cumbria was not very good and we envisaged difficulty in providing good quality audio for the increased numbers in Suffolk. Another reason was our wish to try out written anecdotes. (See Part III, section 4 for further discussion of the different types of starter.)

Despite the different starters the three sessions had a common purpose which was to provide three separate examples of the way of working which we wanted to promote, from which it would be possible to generalise. It was difficult to decide at which point it would be appropriate to present to participants our overview of what our way of working entailed. To talk about it in general terms before participants had particular experiences of what was involved was likely to be confusing. On the other hand, leaving a general picture until three experiences of it had taken place left some participants wondering, sometimes in frustration, why we had not told them earlier what our intentions were. The *Theory of Samenesses*, presented in Part VI, describes our reason for providing experience before theory. Despite some criticisms, we nevertheless believe that this order of presentation is more in keeping with the philosophy behind the way of working, so our presentation in this pack mirrors that of the conferences. (An overview of our way of working, the *Process of Anecdotes → Issues → Action*, is provided in Part IV after various examples of working in this way have been given in Part II.)

COMPOSITION OF GROUPS

We firmly believe that the way of working proposed is relevant to teachers in all phases of education, and so we did not wish to limit the conferences to teachers from just one phase. In constructing groups it was then important to decide whether or how to mix the phases. We decided to have two sorts of groups, one as homogeneous as possible in phase, the other of mixed phase. This worked particularly well in Cumbria, with many participants saying how valuable they had found it to be able to talk to teachers from another phase, whilst yet having opportunity to share common issues with teachers from one's own phase. For this reason we used the same constructions in Suffolk. We recognise that in practice it is more likely that teachers from the same phase will form groups, but it is our experience that the cross-phase discussion proved extremely valuable to those concerned.

The only reservations were to do with access to the video excerpts. Due to comments in Cumbria about the relevance of video showing children of a very different age to those one taught, we decided that video should be used with homogeneous phase groups so that it could be chosen to have more relevance to its viewers.

GROUP WORKING

To give everyone a chance to participate, and encourage everyone to participate, discussions were structured so that individual thinking gave way to discussion in pairs which then led to discussion in groups of from four to seven. A rationale for this 1-2-4 structure is provided in Part III. Participants in Cumbria were so positive about its value that it was continued without question in Suffolk.

FEEDBACK

The views of participants regarding what they had experienced were sought at both conferences. In Cumbria a final whole conference plenary discussion was held at which everyone contributed what had been significant for them, both positively and negatively. In Suffolk, a similar exercise took place but in two large groups. At both conferences evaluation sheets were completed by participants with regard to their expectations for the conference and in how far these were fulfilled. Some remarks from participants, received both verbally and in written form are included in this pack, and others have influenced its writing.

General comments regarded the artificiality of the conference setting and the special nature of the participants. Firstly, it was pointed out that the conference provided a particular environment with advantages and constraints which made the way of working different to its likely operation in practice. We accepted and anticipated that this would be the case. It was nevertheless a source of very valuable experience and feedback. Secondly, the teachers who took part were in the main hand-picked by the advisers, or if not, then were self-selecting in volunteering to give up their time. It was thought that we might therefore be working with a willing and sympathetic audience, which might not be true of teachers more widely. Again we recognise that this was the case. However, it must be said, that we do not wish to force any of these ideas onto any unwilling recipients. We rather offer the ideas in the spirit of having found them valuable ourselves and in the belief that they have potential to be valuable to teachers who seek to work on their own professional development.

CONFERENCE PROGRAMME

The following programme was that of the Suffolk conference, and indicates the different sessions and the order in which they were offered. A-groups were homogeneous in phase; B-groups of mixed phase.

Session 5 corresponds to the Process abstracted in Part IV of this pack. Session 6 began with a plenary presentation of the theory of Part VI of this pack, and the group discussion following it related the theory to working on issues concerning the implementation of the National Curriculum.

The relating of the Anecdoting Process to general themes or matters of concern such as the National Curriculum, TVEI, Cockcroft 243, etc, is taken up in Part V of this pack.

TEACHERS' CONFERENCE

Issues in the Teaching and Learning of Mathematics

●●●

Friday

17.00	House open for registration
18.00	Bar open
19.00	DINNER
20.00	**Session 1**	Whole group activity – 'What it means to work together'. Objectives for the conference
21.30	Informal

Saturday

08.15	BREAKFAST
09.15	**Session 2**	'Issues in teaching and learning – 1' (Video-anecdote) A groups
10.30	Coffee
11.00	**Session 3**	'Issues in teaching and learning – 2' (Written anecdotes) B groups
12.30	Bar open
13.00	LUNCH
14.00	Open for choice
15.30	TEA
16.00	**Session 4**	'Issues in teaching and learning – 3' (Personal anecdotes) A groups
17.30	Informal
18.00	Bar open
18.30	DINNER
19.45	**Session 5**	'A process for Professional Development' Plenary Reflection on this process. B groups
21.15	Informal

Sunday

08.15	BREAKFAST
09.15	**Session 6**	'Applying the process to particular concerns' Plenary Issues related to the implementation of the National Curriculum and working towards attainment targets. Informally convened groups
10.30	Coffee
11.00	**Session 7**	Reflecting on the conference and looking to the future Plenary.
12.30	Bar open
13.00	LUNCH
14.00	Departures

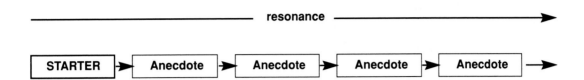

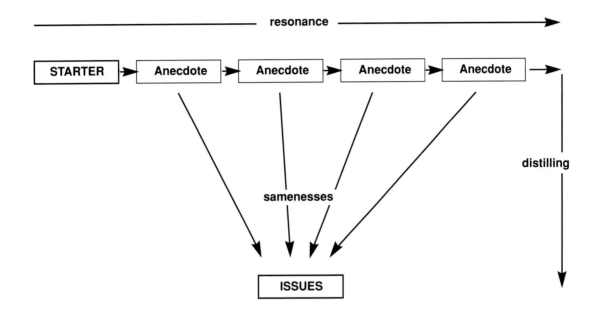

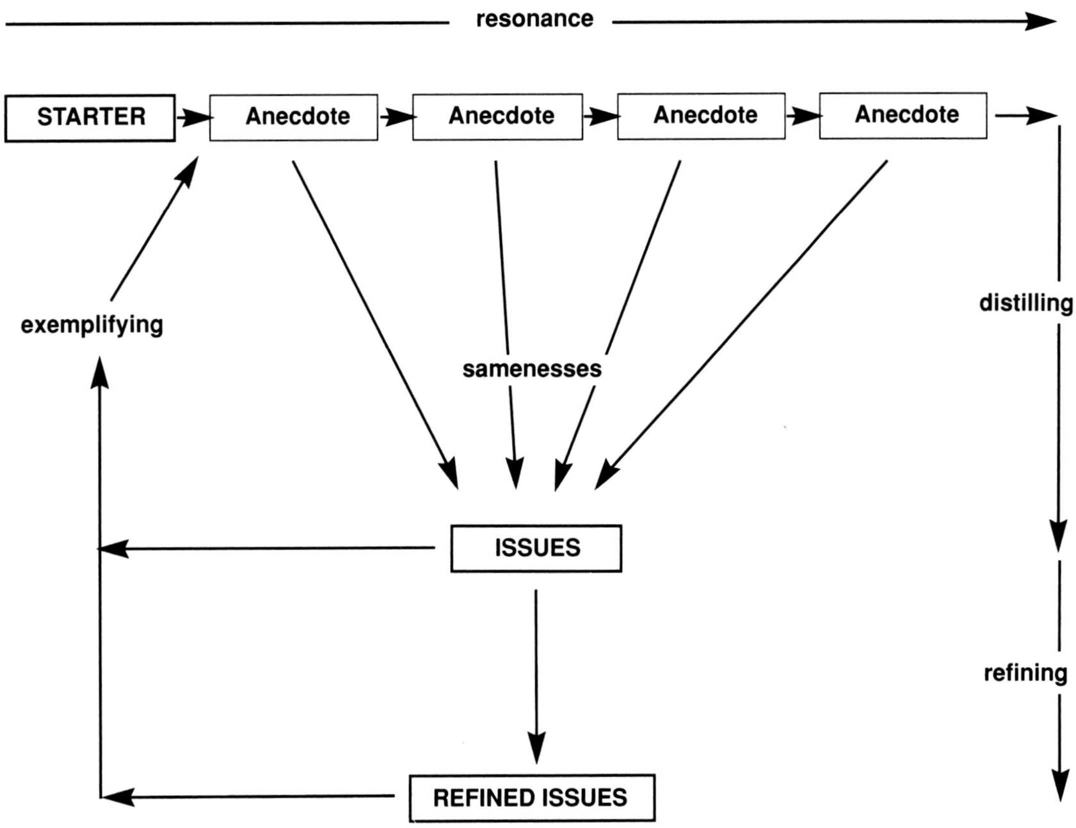
resonance
STARTER
Anecdote
Anecdote
Anecdote
Anecdote
exemplifying
samenesses
distilling
ISSUES
refining
REFINED ISSUES

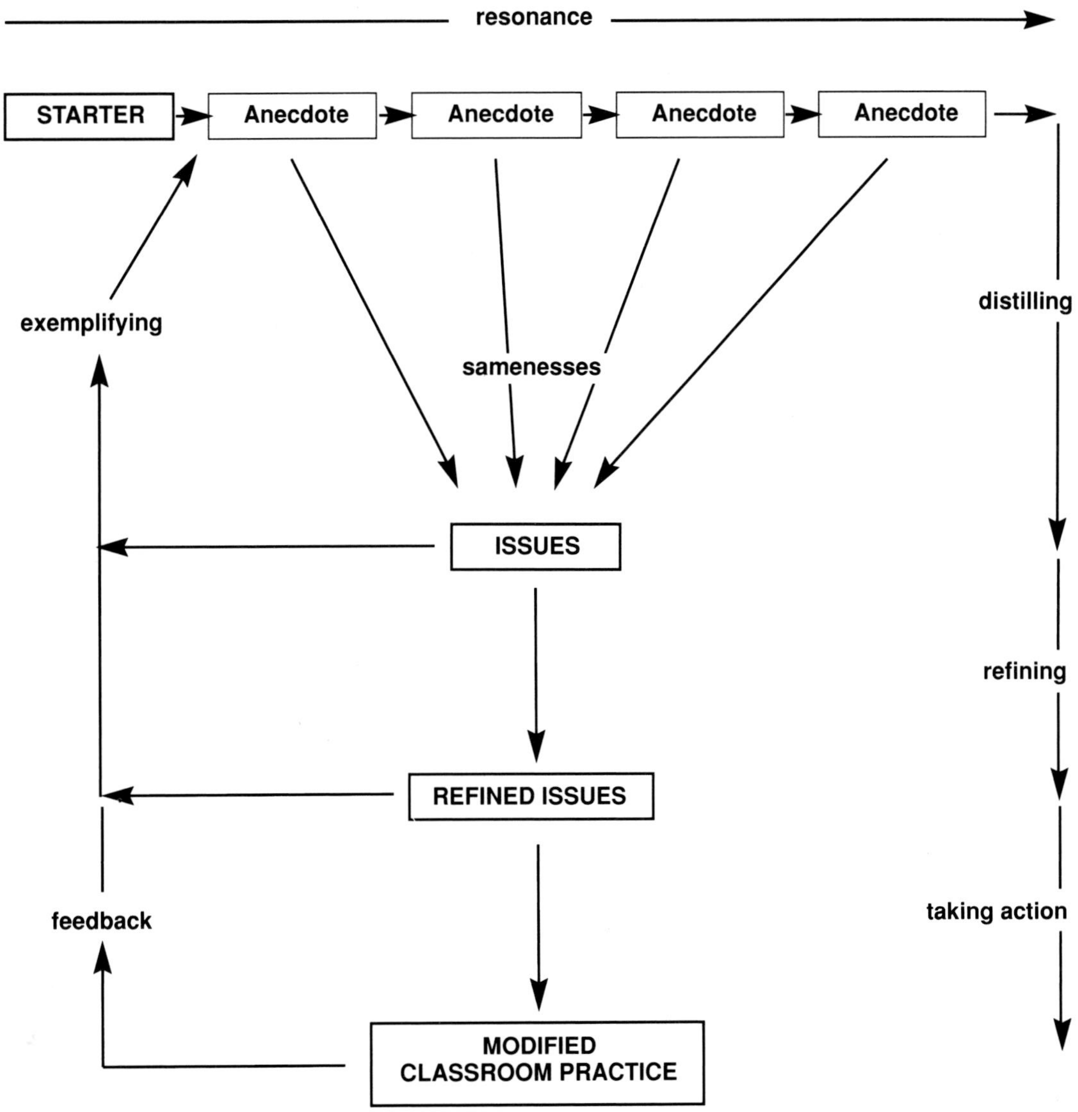
resonance
STARTER
Anecdote
Anecdote
Anecdote
Anecdote
exemplifying
samenesses
distilling
ISSUES
refining
REFINED ISSUES
feedback
taking action
MODIFIED
CLASSROOM PRACTICE